The Science of Geography

Report of the Ad Hoc Committee on Geography
Earth Sciences Division
National Academy of Sciences—National Research Council

National Academy of Sciences—National Research Council
Washington, D. C.   1965

Publication *1277*

Library of Congress Card Catalog Number 65-60052

Preface

The *Ad Hoc* Committee on Geography, Division of Earth Sciences of the National Academy of Sciences-National Research Council, was appointed in May 1963 by Dr. M. King Hubbert, Chairman of the Division. The report presented herewith represents the Committee's consensus as to an appropriate but not exhaustive illustration of geography's research interests, methods, and opportunities. The Committee interprets this report as following the instructions given it by Dr. Hubbert. (Letter of May 18, 1963, pp. vi-vii.) Dr. Hubbert stated that the Committee was to: "1) consider new and promising methods for geography to attain better recognition as a research area, 2) identify geographic concepts and substantive topics that require greater attention or development, and 3) evaluate the potential contribution of geography to the general progress of science." The report that follows presents the Committee's effort to respond to Dr. Hubbert's invitation, and to provide background data for its recommendations.

The Committee therefore limited its review and analysis to those parts of geography that bear upon its future research competence in contributing to the "general progress of science." Except for the training of research workers, the many complex educational aspects of the field were not reviewed. The report also makes no pretension to a methodical treatment of the relation between geographical research and technology. We assume, on the other hand, that if the cause of fundamental science as a whole is served, technological progress also will be served *a priori*. In saying this we add only an emphasis on the already proven relation of geographical research to urban planning, regional planning, transportation, communications, and other space-adjusting techniques.

The Committee, in its review and analysis, also did not attempt an exhaustive coverage of the field. The report is to be considered illustrative in its choice of problem areas, and especially in the choice of references cited as examples of given types of work. Other references of equal merit that do not appear in the bibliography in many cases might have been substituted for or added to those listed. The Committee chose to present the illustrative view in hope that its report would not reach a discouraging length for its prospective readers. Most references are to the work of United States or Canadian geographers. However, occasional reference to European or other foreign research will be found, where it was considered to be in the main current of thought being described by the Committee.

iv

The Committee gratefully acknowledges funds from the Office of Naval Research that covered travel expenses to and from Committee meetings, and the assistance of the Earth Sciences Division office on the Committee's organization and operation. The cooperation and support of the Council of the Association of American Geographers gave valuable reassurance when it was needed. Members of the Committee would particularly like to thank Robert H. Alexander (ONR), Walter H. Bailey (NAS-NRC), Edward B. Espenshade (NAS-NRC and AAG), Arch C. Gerlach (AAG and Geological Survey), Forrest R. Pitts (University of Pittsburgh), Evelyn Pruitt (ONR), Arthur H. Robinson (AAG and University of Wisconsin), and Herbert L. Slutsky (Roosevelt University), for their interest and help. Dr. Pitts' preparation of a paper "Simulation and Diffusion Research in Geography" for the Committee's use was particularly appreciated. Finally, we are grateful for the active interest which Dr. M. King Hubbert took in the Committee's work, and for the encouragement he gave.

A mimeographed first draft of the report was prepared in August 1964 and distributed to 40 American geographers for critical review. Members of the Committee express their warmest gratitude to each of these people, whose collective criticism was invaluable in revising the draft.

EDWARD A. ACKERMAN,
Carnegie Institution of Washington
Chairman
BRIAN J. L. BERRY,
University of Chicago
REID A. BRYSON,
University of Wisconsin
SAUL B. COHEN,
Boston University
EDWARD J. TAAFFE,
Ohio State University
Secretary
WILLIAM L. THOMAS, JR.,
California State College at Hayward
M. GORDON WOLMAN,
The Johns Hopkins University

NATIONAL ACADEMY OF SCIENCES
NATIONAL RESEARCH COUNCIL

Division of Earth Sciences
2101 Constitution Avenue, Washington 25, D. C.

May 18, 1963

Dear ———,

For more than a year, this Division of the Academy-Research Council, through its Executive Committee and Committee on Geography, Advisory to the Office of Naval Research, has been reviewing the status of geography as a field of scientific research. The conclusions of this study are that geography does not have the esteem which it merits by virtue of the importance of its subject matter and that it will not attain proper recognition without some remedial action on the part of the geographic profession. These findings have led to the recommendation that the Division of Earth Sciences establish a Committee on Geography to assess the potential of the field and to propose methods by which geography might advance scientifically.

After consultation with officers of the Association of American Geographers and the American Geographical Society, it is proposed to carry out this recommendation in two stages. Initially, an ad hoc committee, composed exclusively of geographers, will be appointed to 1) consider new and promising methods for geography to attain better recognition as a research area, 2) identify geographic concepts and substantive topics that require greater attention or development, and 3) evaluate the potential contribution of geography to the general progress of science. Upon the completion of this task, estimated to require a year, the Academy-Research Council will consider the feasibility of establishing a formal NAS-NRC Committee on Geography, which would include a number of non-geographers in its membership and which would use the report of the ad hoc committee as a basis for a more thorough analysis of the field of geography and the preparation of appropriate reports and recommendations.

It is my pleasure to invite you to serve on this ad hoc committee on geography, to be chaired by Dr. Edward A. Ackerman. I believe that you will recognize and appreciate the importance of the committee's assignment, and I hope that you will agree to serve as a member. Dr. Ackerman is hopeful that the committee can hold its first meeting during the week

v

of June 3 and I would therefore appreciate knowing if you can come to Washington for several days during that week. As a member of the committee, your travel and living expenses for each of its several anticipated meetings will be paid by the Academy-Research Council.

Because I am personally deeply interested in the future of geography, I look forward to your acceptance of this assignment.

Sincerely yours,

M. KING HUBBERT
Chairman

Contents

Summary

Concepts and Methods

Nearly all branches of science may be related to a few great overriding problems, like the problem of the particulate structure of energy and matter, that of the structure of the cosmos, or the problem of the origin and physiological unity of life forms. Geography's overriding problem, which it shares with other branches of science, is that of a full understanding of the vast system on the earth's surface comprising man and the natural environment.

Of the three great parameters of concern to scientists, space, time, and composition of matter, geography is concerned with two. Geography treats the man-environment system primarily from the point of view of space in time. It seeks to explain how the subsystems of the physical environment are organized on the earth's surface, and how man distributes himself over the earth in his space relation to physical features and to other men. Geography's organizing concept, for which "spatial distributions and space relations" are a verbal shorthand, is a tri-scalar space. The scales comprise extent, density, and succession. Geography's theoretical framework is developed from this basic concept. Settlement (central place) hierarchy, density thresholds, and diffusion theory are examples of theoretical constructs serving specific research.

Geographers have long believed that correlations of spatial distributions are among the most ready keys to understanding existing or developing life systems, social systems, or environmental changes. As geographers undertook such studies in the past they favored heavily the empirical-inductive method. More recently, particularly since the end of the last war, theoretical-deductive methods have been applied. The two currents of thought are now achieving a healthy balance within the research "clusters" that are on the "growing edge" of the field. The same trend also has occurred in the social sciences and biology, particularly through the introduction of systems theory and study techniques. Similar rigorous analytical approaches now offer a common ground for communication among biology, geography, and the traditional social sciences.

The Committee believes that geography is on the threshold of an important opportunity that derives from: (1) the now vital need to understand as fully as possible every aspect of the man-natural environment system, including spatial distributions, throughout the world; (2) the development of a common interest among several branches of science

1

in the overriding problem and its spatial aspects; (3) the development of a more or less common language for communication for the first time among all the pertinent branches of science through mathematical statistics and systems analysis; (4) the development of far more powerful techniques than ever before for analyzing systems problems, including spatial distributions, and (5) a backlog of spatial experience which geographers have accumulated from their spatial perspective and their past dedication to the study of the man-environment complex.

The central section of the report attempts to analyze the interests and competences among geographers that contribute to inter-disciplinary progress in studying the great man-environment system. This analysis is presented in the form of discussions of four different problem areas considered illustrative of the growing edge of geography. The four problem areas are: physical geography, cultural geography, political geography, and location theory. Within each problem area one or more research clusters are found. These are groups with common research interests whose members habitually communicate with one another. For each problem area the Committee evaluates the significance of present and foreseeable research problems, the connection of current working problems with the great overriding problem of man and environment, the relation of the problem area to growing edges in other sciences, and research opportunities considered to be unfulfilled.

Physical Geography

Physical geographers study the physiographic-biotic system as determined by natural and cultural processes, with emphasis on the spatial distribution of the system. Current research in physiography is focused on quantitative observation of landforms and surficial earth processes. These processes involve the movement of water, ice, wind, and soil in different climatic and geologic environments. Clusters of research activity center around the study of rivers, glaciers, coasts, and hill slopes, and the processes acting upon these earth features. Progress has been notable in the study of marine coasts and the arctic environment, both of which have been characterized by close association of geographers and research workers from other fields in common study.

Joint study of plant geography and physiography is flourishing at several centers. The most recent work in climatology and climatography has been on the heat and moisture balance of the earth, on synthetic climatology, and historical climatology.

Three major research opportunities are thought to lie open to physical geographers: (1) a reformulation of basic hypotheses; (2) further observation of physiographic processes in a systems context; and (3) coordination of studies of the natural environment with cultural geography and other clusters of geographic inquiry.

New approaches to the dynamics of process have been provided by recent concepts of equilibria and cycles. The concept of a "threshold" of erosion, for example, is an especially interesting one that should be easily applied to study. One present need is to treat physiographic processes as a complex multi-variate system rather than a previous static sum of landforms and averaged climatic data.

Another increasingly urgent need is for evaluating effects of management and technological changes on the physiographic and biotic environment. Examples of research areas within which the physical geographer's techniques can contribute vital information to an understanding of the man-environment system are: the alteration of drainage basins by several types of water control structures and by "polluting" substances, the reshaping of landscapes by modern earth-moving techniques (including the impending use of nuclear energy therefor), and the study of soil and surface water movement in the presence of continued mechanical cultivation. Expanded study is long overdue for the natural environments in which most of the world's people live.

Cultural Geography

Cultural geographers study the material and non-material phenomena relevant to an understanding of the spatial distribution and space relations of human cultures. Cultural geographers are concerned with the earth as the home of man who, by means of culture, has become the earth's ecological dominant. The usual approach of the cultural geographer is that of studying spatial distributions of the elements or traits of a culture. Two different methods have been used in past cultural geography research: (1) the developmental, which emphasizes study of such relatively long-term processes as cultural evolution, growth, and retrogression; and (2) the functional approach, which focuses on the shorter-term processes of cultural interaction, flow, and movement. The two approaches are complementary, and both are now used in recording and analyzing the effects of man's changing cultures in modifying the face of the earth.

The closest of the past relations of cultural geography with other disciplines have been those with anthropology. Recent cultural geography studies have reflected the advances made by anthropologists in the study of behavior and of value systems. An especially vigorous growing edge in cultural geography has been the study of diffusion.

Specific problem areas in which the techniques of cultural geography seem promising are: (1) study of the nature and rate of diffusion of culture elements, and delineating the evolving spatial pattern of culture contexts; (2) identifying critical geographical zones for contact of culture complexes and discovering incipient "hybrids" or "sensitized" areas; (3) identifying regions of cultural values incompatible with those of major aggressive cultures of today; and (4) identifying regions with cultural values and practices that are causing unstable relations between a society and its natural environment.

Political Geography

The study of political geography is concerned with the interaction of geographical area and political process; it is the study of the spatial distribution and space relations of political process. Its attention centers on the part of the earth occupied by a given political system, subsystem, or systems. Studies may be concerned with territorial phenomena of political systems on (a) supranational, (b) national state, (c) domestic-regional, (d) urban-community, or (e) local special-purpose district basis. Each has a distinctive system or subsystem associated with it.

Two problem areas have been cultivated in the past. One has treated the territorial problems of the national state and subnational governments and their boundaries, and the other has treated resource management. These interests have polarized two distinct clusters of research workers. The general problem area of the resource management group is the study of the internal spatial organization of the giant state, whether federal or another type. The first, or political area group, has been especially concerned with the study of boundaries during its recent activity.

Three problem areas are considered especially significant at the present time: (1) the interfaces of national political systems, particularly in eastern Europe, the southeast Asian area, and Africa; (2) the internal spatial organization of the giant state; and (3) the territorial viability of small national states. Other interesting problems include the spatial distribution of political ideologies, the space relations of voting behavior, and the geography of demagogic control.

Location Theory

Location theory studies have been especially concerned with the development of theoretical-deductive method in geography. They have identified abstract spatial concepts and principles, and have tested these with emphasis upon the interaction of economic, urban, and transportation phenomena in regional systems. Thus the older fields of urban, economic, and transportation geography are being synthesized in a new approach that is the first concerted application of systems theory within geography. In these studies the "dialogue" between the empirical and the theoretical has gone the farthest of any problem area in geography. The cluster of research workers in this area typically has a quantitative bias.

Location theory studies may be classified into four types, each at increasingly higher levels of generalization: (1) study of the static aspects of spatial pattern, like location, spread, density, and geometry; (2) flow linkages between places; (3) temporal dynamics of spatial structure and spatial systems; and (4) normative models leading to "efficiency" solutions. Examples of each type of study are given in the text.

The major opportunity lying before the location theory research workers is the application of methods developed within this problem area to the spatial systems considered in the political, cultural, and physical geography problem areas. This cluster is in a strategic position to improve the dialogue between the theoretical and the empirical in these other problem areas, as it has already demonstrated effectively in the synthesis achieved for the urban-economic-transportation area. Beyond this there are still many opportunities in the areas which have already been treated by this cluster, particularly in the dynamics of spatial systems, and in further development of efficiency studies.

Another opportunity exists for the development of a machine system in which dynamic models of cities or regions might be stored as aids to planning, management, instruction, or other uses that can benefit from observation of dynamic descriptive patterns.

Recommendations

The Committee concludes that the "bridge" position that geography traditionally has occupied, dividing itself between the natural and social science areas, its firm tradition of field observation, and recent rapid growth of theoretical-deductive work within it, offer an increasingly powerful intellectual combination that should be fostered. The Committee proposes a strategy for further research, and catalytic actions for implementation of the strategy.

The Committee recommends as a first step that the National Academy of Sciences-National Research Council establish a senior committee charged with continuing study of the man-natural environment system on the earth's surface. It further recommends expanded support for location theory studies, expansion of research in physical geography, especially as cultural parameters are concerned, expanded studies of cultural diffusion, and attention to those cultural elements most closely related to interaction within the climate-vegetation-erosion system. In political geography it calls specific attention to the study of the spatial organization of a giant state as a general problem, and the study of the interfaces between the political systems of the giant states. In all, it is hoped that the dialogue between the empirical and theoretical can be developed as well as it has been for the present location theory studies. Regional and historical geography are considered especially fitted to contribute from the empirical side.

The catalytic actions for further development of the field suggested are: support for dual-doctoral degrees, support for increased numbers of pre-doctoral fellowships, expanded field research at the pre-doctoral level, support for a continuing series of post-doctoral fellowships, and joint planning of research within two or more problem areas. There are also recommended two research institutes, one in political geography and the other in physical geography, to be located at or near universities having strong geography programs as well as a strong supporting program in non-geographic fields directly related to the institute's concern. It is suggested that each of these institutes be inter-disciplinary, with a staff chosen from geographers and other physical and social scientists interested in the problem area.

It is believed that if an Institute of Political Geography were in existence for ten years it would have a telling impact on our knowledge of political systems, and of the relation of spatial problems to the foreign policy of this country.

The Institute of Physical Geography would focus on the natural system in regions where cultural processes have had a long history and increasing intensity of impact. It is believed that this Institute would make an important contribution to our knowledge of the relation of cultural attitudes to physiographic, biotic, and other environmental changes.

Finally, the Committee recommends that support be given to a continuous effort toward analyzing the needs of geography as data systems change. Being concerned with one of the most complex overriding problems that can be studied, geographers have a vital interest in any improvement in the power of analyzing complex systems. One immediate step in this direction would be the establishment of three or four geographic data centers located at major universities with the latest computing facilities and a potentiality for adding special geographical input, output, and data storage features. These centers would have a major impact upon equipment development and upon training of persons entering location theory studies.

The Committee is certain that, as settlement continues to become more dense in the world and in this nation, the arts of managing space efficiently will be ever more in demand and of ever greater economic importance. Geography seeks the fundamental knowledge that supports the space-managing arts, and contributes to satisfaction of scientific curiosity about the man-natural environment system. The recommended measures would strengthen a field that is on the threshold of some of its most effective work.

I. Geography's Overriding Problem and Organizing Concepts

The Primitive Sense of Place

The modern science of geography derives its substance from man's sense of place and from his curiosity about the spatial attributes of the surface and atmospheric envelope of this planet.

The spatial attributes of the earth's surface have had profound effects upon the hydrosphere and biosphere from the remote periods of their origin. In the hydrosphere, for example, size, shape, latitude, longitude, and orientation of a drainage basin are important determinants of a drainage system's characteristics. In the biosphere, geographical isolation has been an important factor in speciation (Mayr, 1964, 1958; Dobzhansky, 1951),[1] and the space ratio per individual of any specific population may per se cause physiologic effects that influence reproduction and future numbers (Christian, 1963; Kessler, 1963). Space relations[2] are inherently significant in all physiographic and life processes.

A sense of place, a compound of a sense of "territoriality," physical direction, and distance, is very deeply ingrained in the human race. Indeed, it is an almost universal characteristic in higher animals, some of whom have remarkable capacities when compared to human beings. The navigational instincts of many birds are well known and have been frequently studied (Gross, 1940). The navigational capacities of the anadromous fishes are equally remarkable. Territoriality among animals is also a well-known phenomenon. Even insects, like the honey bee, possess these capacities in varying degrees (Von Frisch, 1954; Landauer, 1961). Where high auto-mobility and the beginning of a complex nervous system exists, the attributes of a sense of place are to be found. We are thus concerned with a pattern deeply imprinted in the existence of all higher forms of life.

Without hesitation one may infer therefore that a highly developed sense of place undoubtedly existed in earliest man, no matter how ancient we view his evolutionary emergence to have been. There have been two behavioral manifestations: human curiosity about the attributes of place, and man's ubiquitous identification of his life and activity with

---

[1] A bibliography is given alphabetically for each section at the end of the report.
[2] Space relations are described by considering extent, density and succession.

7

specific places. One led to the exploration of the earth, and the other probably led to all forms of property-holding, including the modern national state. It was no accident that, after the concept of numbers was grasped, some of the first recorded stirrings of science are traceable to the sense of place in early geometry and in early descriptions of localities beyond a home area. It was no accident, too, that a sense of territoriality has pervaded human history from remotest tribal days to the present day, little diminished in its intensity. Our present flowering of new national states, and a fiercely persistent attachment to private property are examples enough. Indeed, one may postulate that combativeness and war have a link to this basic territoriality imprinted on the nervous system of all higher life.

For many centuries, as men worked ever outward from their first confined territorial experience, they depended on accretions of geographical knowledge to widen their concepts, to make something bigger, as it were, out of the primitive territorial instinct. Even into the twentieth century the arts and techniques useful for discovery, exploration, and description of new lands, new regions, and unknown localities were familiar, indeed essential, to leaders in every vigorous advancing society or national group. The primitive individual sense of place was gradually reoriented, reshaped in social terms, and related to a body of knowledge about the spatial attributes of the surface of the earth. The concept of the tribal hunting grounds linked by forest (or other) paths that probably dominated human history for millions of years thus was replaced in advanced societies relatively recently by concepts of family land ownership, trade routes, the boundaries of the principality, kingdom, or nation, and the earth as a sphere.

It is these ancient, indeed almost primeval, bases from which the study of geography springs. First, curiosity has led in the direction of exploration and the study of the content of space in the physical world around us. Hence, physical geography and biogeography were above all a satisfaction of man's curiosity as to how the natural world is spatially organized on the earth's surface. Second, man's sense of place and his needs for sustenance, survival, and enjoyment led to specific human responses to space on the earth's surface. They in turn have become an object of curiosity, and from them have emerged interests in subfields like cultural geography, political geography, and economic geography. Geography therefore is concerned with man's earth-space surrounding and the manner in which his responses alter it and his society.

Geography's Problem and Method

The Committee believes that geography, the study of spatial distributions and space relations on the earth's surface, contributes to treatment of one of the great problems of scholarship. This is a full understanding of the vast overriding system[3] on the earth's surface comprised by man and the natural environment. Indeed, it is one of the four or five great overriding problems[4] commanding the attention of all science, like the problem of the particulate structure of energy and matter, that of the structure and content of the cosmos, or the problem of the origin and physiological unity of life forms.

The three great parameters for any scientific problem, albeit in varying dimensions and attributes, are space, time, and composition of matter. For the problem it treats, that of the man-environment system, geography is concerned primarily with space in time. It seeks to explain how the subsystems of the physical environment are organized on the earth's surface, and how man distributes himself over the earth in his space relation to physical features and to the other men. Space and space relations indeed impose one of the great mediators of the characteristics of any part of the system at any point on the earth's surface. As one of the major subjects concerned with spatial features on the earth's surface, and as the only one traditionally concerned with system interrelations within the space of the earth's surface, geography has a significant place in satisfying man's scientific curiosity.

Geographers have studied the space relations of the man-natural environment system for decades. At a time when few students in other branches of science were concerned with the relations between cultural phenomena and the natural environment, geographers were studying their spatial distributions and attempting correlation studies about them. Geographers' organizing concept, for which "spatial distributions and space relations" are a verbal shorthand, is a tri-scaler space. The scales comprise those of extent, density, and succession. The theoretical framework for investigating the man-environment system is developed from this basic concept. Central place (setttlement) hierarchy, density thresholds, and diffusion theory are examples of theoretical constructs serving specific research.

Geographers believe that correlations of spatial distributions, considered both statically and dynamically, may be the most ready keys to understanding existing or developing life systems, social systems, or environmental changes. They further believe that geography has made a significant contribution in the past to the foundations of knowledge needed to understand subsystems of the man-environment system. Progress was gradual, however, because geographers were few, rigorous methods for analyzing multivariate problems and systems concepts were developed only recently, and few branches of science were committed to study of the man-environment system.

---

[3] System—A functional entity composed of interacting, interdependent parts. A subsystem is a system which is a part of a higher level system.

[4] Overriding problem—A transcendant issue covering many of the problems customarily treated by scientists in theory, experiment, and observation.

The 1965 Opportunity

The situation now has changed enormously. Many aspects of systems theory and study techniques have invaded all of the traditional social sciences, biology, and geography. Rigorous analytical approaches offer a common ground for communication with one or more groups in every pertinent subject. Spurred by world events like the unprecedented increase in population, all science has recognized the overriding problem, the imminent need for understanding the world-wide man-environment system. But even as our capacities to analyze and eventually to understand the man-natural environment system have increased, the problem itself has increased vastly in its proportions. More than ever before there is a social urgency for effective research on it. As Hubbert has aptly shown, the present exponential increases of population and materials consumption in the world cannot continue for very long (Hubbert, 1962, 124-40). The system now is in an unstable condition.

The members of this Committee believe geography has reached a critical stage of opportunity that derives from: (1) the now vital need to understand as fully as possible every aspect of the man-natural environment system, including spatial distributions, throughout the world; (2) the development of a common interest among several branches of science in the overriding problem and its spatial aspects; (3) the development of a more or less common language for communication for the first time among all the pertinent branches of science through mathematical statistics and systems analysis; (4) the development of far more powerful techniques than ever before for analyzing systems problems, including spatial distributions, and (5) a backlog of spatial experience which geographers have accumulated from their spatial perspective and their past dedication to study of the man-environment complex.

Four Basic Assumptions and One Immediate Need

The Committee therefore adopts four premises at the outset of this statement: (a) Scientific progress and social progress are closely correlated, if not equated. (b) Full understanding of the world-wide system comprising man and his natural environment is one of the four or five great overriding problems in all science. (c) The social need for knowledge of space relations of man and natural environment rises, not declines, as the world becomes more settled and more complex, and may reach a crisis stage in the near future. Last, (d) progress in any branch of science concerns all branches, because science as a whole is epigenetic.

The social need for knowledge of space relations means an imminent practical need. As the population density rises and the land use intensity increases, the need for efficient management of space will become ever more urgent. The arts of space management will be in increasing demand, from community planning and industrial plant location to the integrated management of drainage basins. Geographic studies will be irreplaceable components of the scientific support for efficient space management.

Considering carefully these assumptions, we believe that there is an important immediate professional need for integrating geographers' research with that of other scientists to whom the same man-environment problem is important. A question logically follows as to how the geographical profession may most effectively devote its attentions to this need.

We therefore propose in the following sections of the report to analyze the interests and competences within our profession that, cooperatively with other branches of science, can contribute to inter-disciplinary progress in understanding man and his environment. We do this in the form of discussions of four different problem areas illustrative of the "growing edge" of the field.

II. Four Problem Areas and Clusters of Research Interest

The progress of science, to paraphrase James B. Conant (Conant, 1964, xxxi ff.), can be described as a dialogue between the empirical-inductive and the theoretical-deductive methods of thought and investigation. They are not competitive, nor even independent, but two currents, each supplying a unique material for an articulated result as a given branch of science moves forward.

Like some other fields of science, geography until the 1940's did not have balance between the empirical-inductive and the theoretical-deductive approaches, but leaned heavily toward the former. In some degree the imprint of this former predilection is still with the profession. Since the 1940's, however, interest in the theoretical-deductive approach has gained rapidly, as the potentialities of applying topology, geometry, and advanced statistical techniques to geographical problems were comprehended. Interest in the theoretical-deductive is quickening as recognition of the applicability of formal systems analysis spreads, for all geography is concerned with the spatial attributes of systems. The systems concept, indeed, has opened the way toward a flexibility in research that is freeing the field from a past view of the world as a mosaic of regions.

Four general problem areas were chosen to illustrate the present nature of research approaches in geography. They are: physical geography, cultural geography, political geography, and location theory (economic-transportation-urban geography). Within each, one or more clusters[1] of research workers are to be found. These areas of study have been chosen as carefully as possible to give a cross-section of geography's characteristics and potentialities, representing both the empirical-inductive and theoretical deductive work of the present day. *They are not to be thought of strictly in terms of the "fields" or subfields that bore these names in the recent past; they are in reality problem areas that are in transition, in some cases with quite different components than the old "fields."* In one, location theory, the dialogue between the empirical and the theoretical already has gone far; in another, the study of political

---

[1] Cluster—A group of research workers within a branch of science who have achieved a significant degree of professional communication with each other.

area, it has only begun. In all, however, there is a fresh spirit of exploration to discover what are the components of key subsystems in the problem area. The field is where the important problems are; the system concept, rigorously applied, allows geography an almost endless variety of subsystems significant to the overriding problem. This includes comprehensive regional systems, or "functional areas," as well as more extensive functional systems.

In the past these problem areas have been thought of in two main groups: the space relations of the subsystems in the physical-biotic environment, and study of the space relations of man's cultural systems.

The study of space relations in the physical-biotic world, or physical geography, has long been a central interest in geography. Indeed, several specialized studies in the geophysical sciences, like meteorology and physical oceanography, have evolved from physical geography. This area is here illustrated not only because it is a natural beginning to man's curiosity about the distribution of things in the world around him but also because it provides the basic setting into which all men and their cultural systems must be fitted.

The study of the space relations of cultural systems is illustrated by the descriptions of the three other problem areas, those in cultural geography, political geography, and location theory. Thus the greater part of the descriptive matter in this report is concerned with subsystems in the culture area.[2] This division of attention is thought to reflect fairly the proportion of interest in geography as a whole in its emphasis on the physical-biotic and the cultural. However, one of geography's strengths has been its recognition of the interdependence among the systems it studies. The geographer sees the reality of "one world." Even in physical geography studies, which followed an independent course for many years, this interdependence is now stressed. Geography thus is in a unique bridge position between the natural and the social sciences.

In addition to identifying the problem areas of active research interest within geography the Committee attempts to evaluate the significance of present and foreseeable research problems of each area. An evaluation of the significance of research problems requires some identification of the hierarchy of problems connecting our research interests with the overriding problem of understanding the man-natural environment system. It also requires some examination of their relation to growing edges in other sciences, particularly those most closely related to geography. Finally, we examine for each problem area unfulfilled opportunities in our present approaches to research, including obvious needs for habitual inter-disciplinary communication.

---

[2] The part of location theory studies treating space relations in the abstract is an exception. It may be applied universally in geography.

1. Studies in Physical Geography

The Problem Area

Physical geographers study the physiographic-biotic system as determined by natural and cultural processes[3] and the spatial distribution of this system. Many other fields of inquiry either directly or indirectly impinge upon this area of study. Nevertheless, the physical geographer expects to provide a focus for the interpretation of the physical and biological world as a foundation for human activity, spatially considered.

To perform this essential task with competence and insight, the physical geographer must be a specialist. He must be so if he is to be able to select from the mass of specialized inquiry the specific parameters, hypotheses, or approaches which are most appropriate to the relation between man's spatial behavior and his environment. However, the environment of man is not a fixed or given quantity. It is in part a function of man's perception, in part a set of forces which man must modify, and in part the static setting in which he is momentarily placed. The judicious selection of significant descriptive and dynamic parameters of the natural environment through fundamental inquiry is the task of the physical geographer.

A beginning point for physical geography continues to be the study of the distribution of forms and processes in the natural environment. Divided into subspecialties, the field appears to encompass a broad array of major fields such as meteorology, oceanography, hydrology, geomorphology, pedology, and ecology, to each of which the word geography is suffixed. Physical geography once did literally encompass the entire field now thus subdivided. Today, rather than encompassing them, physical geography both draws from and makes common cause with these disciplines in an effort to describe the behavior of air, water, soil, and biota at the surface of the earth, and to explain the covariant distribution of diverse elements of the environment on a particular part of the earth's surface.

Physical geography places particular stress upon the system relations among air, water, soil, and biota (Kalesnik, 1964), upon their distribution into space, and upon their relation to man. The analysis of these complex relations is made manageable because processes involving air and water can often be modeled as closed systems. Where such systems can be recognized, the conditions or state of the system may be measured in terms of temperature, available moisture, organic material, landform change, or other parameters. If the system is cyclical, like the

---

[3] "Process" denotes a succession of physical, biotic, or cultural events dependent on characteristic energizing agents. Thus the physical process of erosion is associated with gravity, hydraulic agents, and atmospheric movement; the vegetative process is associated with the forces of organic genesis, growth, and decay; and technological processes are associated with man's capacity to capture energy from his physical and biotic surroundings and to direct it toward his purposes. (Ackerman, 1958, 5.)

hydrologic cycle, or if it approaches a steady state as in some river channels, the special role of man in the environment may often be appraised by measuring sequential changes in these parameters. Such changes may be associated with historical changes in land use and development or they may be induced by artificial manipulation of the existing environment. Thus, concepts of the interrelation of many elements in the environment, their distribution in space, and their behavior as systems provide fundamental bases for physical geographic study. They are logical beginnings for an understanding of the man-environment system.

Current Activity

Study of physical geography formed the backbone of geography from its beginning until early in the present century. Geographers were universally concerned with descriptions of the atmosphere, the oceans, and the land. Where natural phenomena appeared to impinge directly upon human affairs, geographers were especially interested in the relation between the two, although the study of the earth itself in the presence or absence of man provided a valid area of inquiry. Then for about 30 years geographic interest in the physical earth appeared to wane. The waning trend is now reversing.

Although the activities described below do encompass workers in a variety of specialties in a number of different geographic regions, communication among many of them is very active. In addition many investigators share common concepts and approaches. In both climatology and physiography dynamic equilibria and analyses of transport processes are receiving strong emphases. Similarly, current work in plant geography emphasizes the relation between plant distribution and the dynamics of surficial earth processes.

a. *Physiography.* Quantitative observations of landforms and surficial earth processes provide one of several foci of current research in physiography. These processes involve the movement of water, ice, wind, and soil in different climatic and geologic environments. Research has been concerned with the evolution and maintenance of specific landforms dominated by one or more of these forces. Thus clusters of activity center around the study of such features as rivers, glaciers, coasts, or hillslopes and the processes acting upon them. Although the dual threads of process and measurement are not equally well developed in each of these areas, significant activity is apparent in all four. The geographic contribution in these areas varies considerably. It looms quite large in coastal studies and, particularly in Europe, on studies of slope processes.

The range from theory to field observation is at the moment perhaps best integrated and most comprehensively covered in the study of glaciers. Recent theoretical formulations of the mechanics of glacier flow (Nye, 1959) have revolutionized the analysis of glaciers themselves and of glacier response to climate. These analyses have provided a framework for observations of the movement of glaciers and for the correlation of such observations with climatic data (Meier, 1960; Heusser and Marcus, 1964).

In the study of rivers, correlative measurements of river hydraulics, alluvial forms, and drainage basin characteristics have begun to provide a more complete picture of the behavior of the entire drainage system in response to climatic and geologic controls (Leopold and Maddock, 1963; Sundborg, 1956). Extension of these findings has suggested theoretical hypotheses of the probable characteristics of alluvial landforms assuming the operation of specific physical constraints related to transport of sediment and water (Langbein, 1964).

A comprehensive program of coastal studies at the Coastal Studies Institute, Louisiana State University, Baton Rouge, emphasizing historical, geomorphic, and sedimentary relationships is demonstrating the value of concentrated attack upon a single class of geographic problems. These studies include observations of coastal processes involving waves, wind, and rivers, and their effect on beaches, bars, deltas, dunes, cliffs, mudflats, and other coastal features (Morgan, 1951; Russell, 1962). The association of current processes and resultant stratigraphy and form are particularly valuable in developing a sound foundation for interpretation of coastal evolution. At their best these inquiries utilize techniques in archaeology (McIntire, 1958), botany (Sauer, 1961), and history (Dunbar and Kniffen, 1957), and thereby demonstrate one of the stimulating facets of modern physiography. It draws from and contributes to cultural, historical, and economic geography. Study of coasts from tropical to arid regions has begun to show both the universality of some coastal features and also the extreme complexity of the processes causing their evolution. This system involves the interaction of climate, vegetation, and coastal morphology. At the same time laboratory and field studies of the mechanics of coastal processes provide principles and data which can be utilized in both physiographic and sedimentation studies (Eagleson, et al., 1953; Inman, 1964).

Careful measurements of hillslope forms were pioneered by Strahler (1950) and his associates. Although the number of studies remains small, significant efforts at observation and measurement of slope processes are also under way (Savigear, 1952; Schumm, 1956). A few, particularly those in arctic and periglacial regions where hillslope processes operate rapidly enough to be easily measured, begin to provide data with which to evaluate the relative magnitude of such forces as solution, running water, and mass movement in different regions (Rapp, 1960; Jäckli, 1957). These more detailed studies can also be used in comparisons of denudation rates in different regions, a subject of interest to both geophysicists (Langbein and Schumm, 1958), and to cultural geographers concerned with land erosion resulting from the activities of man (Haggett, 1961).

From a regional standpoint, the far north continues to provide perhaps the most fruitful environment for regional studies in physical geography. In Canada, the United States, England, and Sweden, universities and governmental agencies are providing fundamental knowledge of many aspects of the northern physical environment. These studies range from analyses of glacier mechanics and response to climate, noted earlier, to geomorphic interpretations of modern and fossil landforms (Mackay, 1963). A striking feature of much of this work is the close association of geographer, physicist, biologist, climatologist, archaeologist, and geologist. Originally dictated in part by expensive logistic problems, as in polar research, this collaboration has proved most fruitful.

b. *Climatology.* By contrast with geomorphology, climatic research has not undergone an extensive recent renaissance among geographers. Climate is recognized as of great importance to man, and is the most variable of the components of the natural environment. A large fraction of professional geographers expresses a teaching and research interest in climatology, but relatively few significant research papers have been produced in recent years. Some notable exceptions are exemplified by the work of Thornthwaite (1961) on the heat and moisture balance of the earth's surface and Curry (1962) on the relation of climatic probabilities and agricultural practices. Several studies have also led to better definition of climatic elements and climatic zones (Flohn, 1957).

Possibly the most stimulating recent work in climatology has dealt with synthetic climatology or "climatonomy" (Lettau, 1962), and dynamic climatology (e.g., Hare, 1962). Synthetic climatology attempts the quantitative explanation of local and regional climate using as a basis turbulent transfer theory and other fundamental physical principles. Dynamic climatology uses the recent explosive growth of general circulation theory and large-scale machine computation to describe and explain the broad features of the climate. The research in these fields has not yet entered into the mainstream of geographic thought about the man-environment system. This gap in communication among geographers provides an attractive opportunity for constructive action.

Two other largely unexploited areas of climatic research—the microclimatology of cities, and historical climatology—are especially significant in studying the man-natural environment system. With increasing urbanization, city microclimates merge into a macroclimate that is man-made. The concomitant air pollution then becomes an ominous as well as significant factor. The literature on this problem is of great interest to the geographic profession—but needs interpretation and utilization. On the other hand, a most fruitful collaboration of climatologists and historians with peripheral sciences is adding detail and certainty to our knowledge of past climates (Bryson and Julian, 1963). This research has a significant relation to historical geography.

c. *Physiography and Biotic Geography.* A close association of plant geography and physiography continues to flourish at several centers. Studies by Sauer (1961) and others elucidate the fundamental relation between vegetation, geology, and geomorphic processes on the coast.

These inquiries and those of atoll research workers demonstrate how vegetation adjusts to storms, to tides, and to variations in geology. In a completely different environment, Goodlett's floristic geographic studies with Hack (1960) and others place renewed emphasis upon mapping and analysis of spatial distribution as a means of shedding new light on the relation between geomorphic processes and the distribution of vegetation. Studies of the distribution of forest species have shown marked covariance with hydrologic and lithologic factors. In addition, studies of the species distribution of the modern flora have a significant by-product in providing a model of relation between pollen assemblages and distribution of vegetation to interpret past landscapes.

A strikingly successful liaison of botany, geomorphology, history, and economics is illustrated in the study of the origin of the coastal area of eastern England known as the Broads (Lambert et al, 1960). Collaborative efforts in the far north, as noted elsewhere, have provided insight into the interaction of process and vegetation (Drury, 1956). A similar close interrelation is observable between distribution of tree species on flood plains and the dynamics of floods, spring flows, winter ice cover and disposition of sediment in a humid temperature environment (Sigafoos, 1961). Although these and other studies in plant geography are closely related to work in ecology, the latter has perhaps given greater emphasis to physiologic and organic aspects of vegetation and has been less concerned with distribution and physiographic process.

The physical and biogeographic effects of man's wholesale modification of his environment provide new impetus to both biologically and physically oriented studies of the landscape.[4] For example, water control structures, by altering the regimen of streams, produce significant changes in water quality, channel morphology, and vegetation in both upstream and downstream reaches of natural channels (Wolman, 1964; Churchill, 1957). Similarly, sequential changes associated with large-scale construction operations on the land produce initially large concentrations of sediment to streams. Upon completion of construction large areas are covered by impermeable surfaces and streams are starved of sediment. This sequence of events may cause decreased channel conveyance, increased flooding, vegetative growth in channels, reduced oxygenation of bottom waters, and changes in fish population and microbiota. Later runoff from roads and streets may vary in both quality and quantity from its former condition; the nature of these changes is known in detail in only a very few places. In most areas information, if it exists, is primarily qualitative.

Physical Geography and Other Subjects

Renewed interest and inquiry in physical geography has been closely associated with significant expansion of research and research techniques

---

[4] Landscape—the visible surface of the earth, including cultural alterations thereof.

in allied fields. Analyses of the behavior of rivers have accompanied theoretical and laboratory studies of fluid dynamics, sediment transport, and energy changes associated with mobile boundaries. A close working relation between field observation and laboratory experiment has revealed fundamental relations between flow, sediment transport, bed configuration, and channel form. New instrumentation permits field measurement of simultaneous changes in parameters.

Advances in theoretical statistics, techniques of sampling, computer simulation, and computer analysis of data have been readily applied to physical geography. The National Research Council-Earth Sciences Division Symposium in 1963 on computers in geography and geology demonstrated that programs have been developed to compute trend surfaces, evaluate sampling programs, correlate data distributed in space, and simulate diffusion processes in physical and other geography. Statistical analysis of tree ring data, for example, has called into question previously reported cyclical patterns in some physical geographic data. Correlation studies of tree rings (Bryson and Dutton, 1961) have also demonstrated the need for examining closely the relation between weather conditions and rates of tree growth, and lag-time between tree response and variations in weather elements.

One of the most interesting and productive symbiotic relations between physical geography and other fields has developed where the only record of history is that reposing in the landscape, in recent stratigraphic evidence, in floral or faunal gene pools, in archaeological sites, or other similar phenomena.

Archaeological sites provide one of the most significant meeting grounds of modern physical geography and other disciplines. Virtually all field observational disciplines seem to meet at such sites. Here the tools and insights of the physiographer, cultural geographer, botanist, pedologist, zoologist, anthropologist, historian, and archaeologist contribute to the understanding of both local history and the evolution of man and society. The recognition that much of the evidence is physical and stratigraphic has led to a progressively closer alliance of physical geographers, cultural geographers, and archaeologists. Careful reconstruction of the climatic and physiographic environment is essential if historical generalizations relating to man and his environment are to be valid. This subject interdependence has been clearly recognized in many recent excavations in the Middle East (Braidwood and Howe, 1960), although contributions by geographers have been limited.

Cytogenetic studies are contributing significantly to cultural geography and to cultural history with information on the genetic composition and origin of cultivated plants. Results from these studies provide unique keys to the history and sequence of contacts among diverse cultures in many parts of the world (Smith and MacNeish, 1964). These relations in turn shed light on the way in which different peoples have come to terms with their environment and on the sources of inspiration and ideas which aided them in doing so.

With improved dating methods, the tie between archaeologists and physiographers and the other fields also is being strengthened. As the physiographer helps to reconstruct the environment of the past, he enhances the archaeologist's interpretations. At the same time, as the latter refines his time scale, the physiographer is provided with new and powerful tools for measuring rates of surficial earth processes (Miller and Wendorf, 1958). Present knowledge of these rates is universally meager yet of fundamental importance to any understanding of surficial earth processes in terms of basic geophysics or as a reference level in evaluating the effects of changes in land use or climate.

Some Areas of Future Emphasis in Research

Three major opportunities confront research workers in physical geography: (1) further reorientation of study toward a dynamic systems concept of physiographic processes; (2) much increased observation of surficial processes, particularly in conjunction with theoretical work; and (3) study of the interrelation between physiographic processes and man's activities.

The study of the earth for its own sake and the study of the spatial aspects of man's use of the earth are inextricably bound. By definition such studies are fundamental to an analysis of the man-environment system. A view of this area of inquiry may be obtained from a consideration of a hierarchy of basic problems. Although some current work mirrors this hierarchical structure, the need for studies at several levels in the hierarchy is critical. It must also be recognized that past processes in a given region may have differed markedly from present processes.

Reformulation of Basic Hypotheses. Several approaches to these major problems can be considered. First, in physiography, general principles of landform development, such as those proposed years ago by William Morris Davis and Walther Penck, must be reformulated so as to evaluate all the physical and biological factors entering into the basic hypotheses. Presumably such evaluations will be easier if quantitative relations can be established to describe the system. Such a fundamental formulation must take into account the wide spectrum of possible combinations of climatic and physiographic parameters found in nature.

Already an excellent beginning in this direction has been made. A significant approach to the dynamics of process has been provided by recent concepts of equilibria and cycles. Cycles are best exemplified in models of the heat balance or hydrologic budget of drainage basins and other regional systems of the earth's surface. To the extent that soil and water systems can be postulated to operate at a steady state, it is possible to evaluate input, output, and changes in storage within the system. Concepts like dynamic equilibrium and steady state (Chorley, 1962), or the maintenance of particular landforms as a consequence of the continuous interaction of specific processes and rock materials, are powerful tools in physical geographic studies. The concept of a budget or balance affords a simple mechanism for evaluating the dynamic and spatial relationships between different quantities. The concept of a threshold of erosion, for example, provides a criterion that can be verified and that can be used to evaluate changes in surface form accompanying known or predicted changes in external forces.

These concepts of the physical environment, drawing upon new findings from diverse sciences, are modifying the traditional tendencies to treat environment as a static sum of landforms and averaged climatic data rather than as a complex multivariate system. This reorientation of physiographic study of the natural environment is essential if it is to be truly related to economic analysis, resource management, and other problem areas of geography—an association providing a major opportunity and responsibility of physical geography.

Observation of Earth Surface Processes. A second need is for clear and accurate descriptions of surficial processes. These processes include movement of soil and rock by running water and mass movement, transport of moisture from the atmosphere to soil to plants and back to the atmosphere, disintegration of rock and circulation of solutes, and movement and mixing of diverse materials in the atmosphere. The collective action of these processes, their space distribution and relation to human activity are the physical geographers' foci of attention. Of particular importance is an evaluation of the comparative importance of different processes under different climatic and geologic regimes.

Considering the variety and extent of observations to be made, it is not surprising that the characteristics of the environment of man at the surface of the earth, the interface of the atmosphere, soil, and ocean, are still poorly known. In generalized terms the mechanisms at work, their relation to vegetation, and the manner in which they mold the landscape are scarcely described or understood over much of the earth's surface. Yet these observations are not only absolutely essential for further theoretical progress in this science, they are also vital to the most effective progress in many of the arts by which man manages or develops resources, or otherwise transforms his environment.

The need here is for the observation of physiographic units as interconnected systems, using the newer conceptual tools and statistical aids. A great many data have been, and are being collected on hydrology, erosion, vegetative cover, and climatic elements; but measurement and analysis of their performance as local or regional systems are rare indeed. Such studies are essential if physical geography is to contribute most effectively to an understanding of the earth and to the progress of society.

The Interrelation Between Physiographic Process and Man's Activities. In addition to the studies of process an increased understanding must be sought about the way in which the natural environment is modified by man and the consequences of such environmental change. Satisfactory answers to such questions require detailed knowledge of both process and form at times and in regions where man has markedly altered the land and where he has not. A better description and understanding of the relation between organic and inorganic systems is particularly needed.

It is now obvious that man's activities have greatly increased their power within a relatively few years to alter the natural environment, both because of the rapidly rising world population, and because of the great impact of technologic development. For example, the changes collectively described by the term "pollution," and regulation of streams by reservoir or other means have greatly changed surface and ground water characteristics in the parts of the world where most people live.

As another example, the already profound effects of modern earth-moving techniques appear certain to be deepened in the near future, as the employment of nuclear explosives comes into use. Finally, chemistry and machine technology have been responsible for vast increases in agricultural productivity in many regions of the world, and their application is spreading more widely with each passing year. Although most investigators recognize that agriculture alters soil properties, few studies have been made of the nature, permanence, or importance of these changes.

An increasing variety of phenomena related to physiographic events is being examined from cultural points of view. Illustrations are found in recent studies of the nature of human perception of the natural environment, and of the role of economic, historic, and psychological factors in adjustment to specific environments like flood plains (White et al., 1958; Stone, 1962; Kates, 1962). Yet response to environment cannot be evaluated definitively in the absence of accurate, detailed knowledge of the environment itself.

It is time that the physiographically powerful forces produced by man's culture be recognized as one of the parts of the system that the physical geographer studies. Yet, such fundamentals as the relation of threshold of erosion to landscape changes, the frequency of sequential events such as drought-fire-mudflows, or snowfall-snowmelt-avalanches, the variable composition of dissolved and clastic load in rivers, the response of biota in rivers and lakes to temporal changes in physical factors, and the chemical and physical effects of cultivation on soils, remain inadequately understood. The past concentration of physiographic effort on arid regions, arctic regions, and the marine coastal environment needs to be supplemented by much expanded study of the natural environments in which most of the world's people live. Indeed, considering its basic nature, such study is long overdue.

2. Studies in Cultural Geography

The second important set of components in the man-land system is that of culture.[5] These are the attributes that distinguish man as a member of a social group.

Culture and Cultures

Cultural geographers, through application of the concept of culture, seek understanding of the spatial distribution and space relations of man and those features on the earth's surface which have been produced or modified by human action. To this end they have focused their attention upon study of the differences from place to place in the ways of life of human communities and their creation of man-made or modified features. In such research the holistic concept of *culture* is implicit, and the partitive concept of *cultures*[6] becomes much more significant for cultural geography. The idea of cultures has a lower level of abstraction that recognizes the pluralism of particular ways of life and distinguishes one human group from another. The partitive concept concerns the thousands of more or less cohesive segments or subsystems, (e.g., Japanese culture, Navaho culture) that comprise the whole. The concept of cultures as subsystems offers a means for systematic classification of human beings into well-defined groups according to verifiable common characteristics (Augelli, 1958). It also offers a means of classifying the phenomena or processes associated with people who habitually share communication and inhabit a common territory.

Cultural geographers are not concerned with analysis and explanatory description of the totality of cultures in all their forms and functions. They study the material and nonmaterial phenomena and processes relevant for an understanding of the spatial distribution and spatial relations of cultures. Emphasis thus far has been upon the past achievements, present capacities, and future capabilities of human communities to produce and to consume resources and, in so doing, to create and to change their habitats on the earth's surface (McBryde, 1947). Cultural

---

[5] Culture is the distillate of total human experience, the possession of which not only distinguishes mankind from other living forms but also sets man apart as a unique evolutionary product. Culture, as a holistic system, distinguishes processes and phenomena which are artificial (man-made) from those which are physical (inorganic) or biotic (organic).

"Culture consists of patterns, explicit and implicit, of and for behavior acquired and transmitted by symbols, constituting the distinctive achievement of human groups, including their embodiment in artifacts. The essential core of culture consists of traditional (i.e., historically derived and selected) ideas and especially their attached values. Culture systems may, on the one hand, be considered as products of action; on the other as conditioning elements of further action." (Kroeber and Kluckhohn, 1952, 181).

[6] Cultures—functional parts of the abstract whole—total human culture; important for study because men with different cultures react differently to similar physical-biotic environments.

geography is thus "earth-bound"; the earth is the home of man who, by means of culture, has become the ecological dominant.

Sub-groups Engaged in Active Research

American cultural geographers are composed of two subgroups of research workers: (1) those who study their own culture, and (2) those who engage in foreign-field research and use foreign languages as tools for research and analysis of cultures other than their own. This sub-grouping is not simply the result of training, but reflects the complexity of problems chosen for study. For example, in studying and reporting on his own culture a geographer knows that the people being observed and the audience for the report are of the same culture. To study and interpret a foreign culture the geographer must successfully carry through "cross-cultural" communication. In such a situation the cultural geographer has to cope with his audience's American predilection for economic explanation of all phenomena. When presenting the results of foreign-field research a cultural geographer must give much descriptive detail to compensate for readers' ignorance of the other culture's postulates and beliefs (Pelzer, 1945).

Problem Areas in Cultural Geography

The foundations of cultural geography were laid in Europe, with the work of Ratzel, Hahn, Brunhes, Fleure, Meitzen, Hettner, Vidal de la Blache. In the United States cultural geography has had a gradual but productive growth over the past 50 years. Much effort has been spent in disentangling it from the relicts of post-Renaissance European thought that viewed nature in a mechanical analogue devoid of intelligence or of life, with the parts designed, arranged, and set going for a definite purpose by an intelligent mind outside of nature (Collingwood, 1945, 8-9; 1950, 93-132). Such a view (nature ordered by the intelligence of a Divine Creator) supported scientific study focused upon unchanging matter or substance and upon the "laws" or unchanging rules which explained change. From such thought was derived the idea of nature as non-man, that which lies all about but outside of man; hence, there developed the concepts of "man and nature" or "man versus nature." This conceptual separation of man from nature did much to postpone cultural geography's fullest contributions to fundamental research. The establishment of scientific geography in central Europe during the early nineteenth century insured the inclusion of such dichotomous thought in geography's concern with the earth created as the home of man. Geography often was defined as the study of man and the earth. In a sense it was concerned with the study of two supposedly distinct systems.

Modern science focuses upon change itself, recognizing that through time things begin to exist, then later cease to exist. On the earth new material and non-material phenomena are constantly emerging. From the physical earth emerged the organic which in turn evolved man who developed culture as a new mechanism for adaptation and change supplementing natural selection. Man, viewed thus, is a part of nature.

Science now concentrates on the study of processes, often described as development, evolution, improvement, and progress. All are movements occupying space and taking time. Cultural geography, as a part of science, now also concentrates on the study of processes. The differences in methods among cultural geographers depend upon the process or processes of change selected for study. How the external world appears depends upon the length of time of observation—one minute, one hour, one day, one year, one century, one millennium. Different processes take time periods of different lengths. What problems man can observe are determined by space limits and time limits. Our limits for observation are human-bounded, because man is a creature of a definite size range and living at a definite rate over an average time span of about 70 years. The processes upon which the geographer concentrates are those whose time phase and space range are within human limits of observation.

Ackerman (1958, 22-26) suggested that the significant processes for geographic study are short range (from the point of view of earth history). Assuming that cultural processes now are the major forces altering the continually changing earth-space content, he outlined at least three processes fundamental to cultural geography:

(1) Demographic Movement
   Natural increase and net migration of people (numbers of people)
   Traditions of material consumption (social qualities of people)
(2) Evolution of Organization and Administration
   Political territories; economic corporations
   Systems of communication (including education)
(3) Development of Technology
   Resource-converting techniques [7]
   Space-adjusting techniques [8]

A Hierarchy of Problems

As his usual approach to a problem, the cultural geographer studies the spatial distribution of elements or traits of a culture. One appropriate technique is to record observations by plotting distributions on a map. The analysis of the content of a culture into elements or traits

---

[7] Resource-converting techniques—Those arts which turn the materials of the physical world and the life-products of the biotic world to satisfaction of the needs of man. Land-use technology is an example.

[8] Space-adjusting techniques—Those arts which either shorten the effective distance of travel and transportation or permit intensification of space employment beyond that possible on the natural land surface. Civil engineering and architecture are examples.

(religious beliefs, languages, voting behavior, prehistoric artifacts, barns, fences, house types) is the important beginning to problem recognition but does not in itself constitute a problem. A thorough knowledge of culture content and form must precede an understanding of the functioning of a culture or of the process of cultural change. Such thorough knowledge may require decades of painstaking descriptions of relatively small areas (Kniffen, 1936). Much important research in cultural geography has been of an inventory character in order to create "building-blocks" so that further research may be cumulative rather than repetitive.

Two different integrative methods have been used widely in cultural geographic research. These are: (1) developmental, which emphasizes the time depth of such relatively long-term processes as cultural evolution, origin and diffusion, cultural growth and retrogression; and (2) functional, which focuses upon the short-term processes of cultural interaction, spatial organization, and flow or movement.

In American geography the developmental or genetic orientation was established by Carl O. Sauer (1931, 623) in the late 1920's with a concern, as in geomorphology, for explaining both the present scene and the dynamics of landscape change through historical reconstruction of the successive agents (cultures) active in an area, beginning with the earliest and proceeding to the present. From a quarter-century association with anthropology at the University of California, Berkeley, the label "culture-historical" often shortened to become simply "historical geography," was derived from this approach. Its method rests largely upon direct field observations, combined with the use of available historical data. By piecing together evidence from culture-trait and trait-complex distributions, linguistics, place names, the characteristics of domesticated plants and animals, archaeological artifacts, documents, oral traditions, and other sources, this developmental approach seeks to determine: (1) the origin in place and time of specific cultural features (e.g., Spencer and Hale, 1961); (2) the routes, times, and manner of their diffusion (e.g., Sauer, 1952); (3) the distribution of former and present cultural areas[9] (Mikesell, 1961); and (4) explanatory descriptions of the character of former and present cultural landscapes[10] (Broek, 1932).

---

[9] Culture area—A region in which the culture is relatively uniform, as empirically determined from the mapping of trait and trait-complexes.

[10] Cultural landscape—The composite of man-made features in an area (e.g., dwellings and other structures, cultivated plants and man-induced wild vegetation, and altered landforms such as gully and sheet erosion and silt deposits in stream valleys and coastal margins). Broadly conceived, such a view of landscape includes all man-induced alterations of and additions to the earth's physical-biotic surface, some utilitarian and some non-utilitarian, many purposeful, and some the indirect, even unintended, results of human activity. This concept stems from the 1920's when geographers were seeking to delimit the subject matter of geography and increase objectivity in observations by focusing upon visible elements of material culture that give character to area.

Implicit is a concern for culture changes which occur slowly, often taking more than single lifetimes in which to be readily apparent.

The second integrative method in American cultural geography had its principal center in middle western United States (Platt, 1953, 488). Attention has been directed to the works of man as functional problems in the local environment (for example, types of buildings and farm crops distinguished by utility and setting), or to data on human interaction in the endeavor to define regularities in spatial arrangement and flow phenomena (for example, studies of central-place hierarchy that indicate conformal distributions of settlements in many parts of Anglo-America and other major culture areas of the world). The functional approach emphasizes the observation of the present-day scene to determine how things are organized and operated. The key word is "process": what are the cultural processes that create landscapes and human attitudes? Studies are usually direct: to discover, to analyze, and to describe step by step the actual activities creating a given cultural feature. Cultural changes of primary interest are those occurring with some suddenness, often clearly recognized by the persons involved.

Recent cultural geographers recognize the value of both the cultural-historical approach and the functional-pattern approach.

The relation of research in cultural geography to the overriding problem of geography, the need for understanding the world-wide man-environment system, has been direct and significant. As soon as the dominant thought in cultural geography had shifted from the view of "man and nature" to that of "man as the new emergent in nature," the way was open for significant contributions. Modern cultural geography has taken the lead among the branches of science in recognizing that man, as a result of culture, has spread over the world, has learned to adapt to the most diverse climates and habitats, and in so doing has drastically altered the landscape of large parts of the earth (Thomas, 1956; Carter, 1964). Cultural geographers record and analyze the effects of man's changing cultures in modifying the face of the earth; the emphasis is upon what has happened, is happening, and the determinants of what is likely to happen to the earth's surface.

Relation to Other Branches of Science

The closest past relation of cultural geography to other disciplines has been with anthropology (Forde, 1934; Stanislawski, 1947; Brookfield, 1961, 1962). The concept of culture has been given greatest exploration and conceptual development during this century by anthropologists. Since 1950 there has been a high degree of unanimity concerning the value of the concept. It has become common for anthropologists to discuss their subject in terms of their key concept, "culture."

Anthropological interest, by and large, is now shifting away from past treatment of material phenomena. Two major growing edges in contemporary cultural anthropology have had a profound effect in this change: the emphases on (1) behavioral studies and (2) value systems.

Behavioral studies seek means of deeper penetration into analyses of the functioning of a culture and to validate (through refinement of predictions about behavior) the cultural constructs depicted by anthropologists.

More important for geography is the anthropological growing edge focused upon value systems. Values are those configuring principles of a culture (the values of a way of life) that lace together the cultural whole and determine the particular patterns (rules or understandings) that motivate and guide its behavior. Values are the essence of cultural study, for without them one cannot comprehend the "slant" of the culture or its organizing principles. Of prime importance for cultural geography is that part of value systems expressed in the phrase (man's *attitudes* toward his physical-biotic environment." Much can be predicted about the probable directions of change in a given part of the earth's surface (e.g., rates of consumption of resources) if one knows the attitudes of the occupying cultures, i.e., passively submissive to natural forces, or slowly adjusting to physical-biotic changes, or seeking a balance or harmony (long-term equilibrium), or actively modifying the physical-biotic surroundings and creating an increasingly artificial habitat, or determined to gain power over and to control natural processes. Influenced by anthropological thought, many cultural geographers are coming to realize that ideas, attitudes, and other non-visible entities of a culture are of importance in understanding spatial distributions and space relations of phenomena (Isaac, 1959, 1961-1962).

Another joint interest, representing a growing edge, is with sociology, especially in research on spatial processes that lend themselves to computer analysis and the application of simulation techniques. Emphasis has been upon the study of diffusion (such problems as the spread of new ideas, the extent and direction of local migration, and marriage contacts). The geographer Hägerstrand (1950, 1962) of Lund, Sweden, used the Monte Carlo simulation technique to replicate within a computer a diffusion process, person-to-person contacts over space. In cultural geography techniques of simulation also are being applied in such studies as the diffusion of a farm subsidy in Sweden (Hägerstrand, 1953), the spread of hand tractors in Japan (Pitts, 1962), the process of frontier settlement (Bylund, 1960), and the acceptance of innovation in Latin America (Deutschmann, 1962).

There are long-established intellectual joint interests between cultural geographers and economic historians, agricultural historians, human ecologists (Theodorson, 1961), and economic botanists. One of the most active research interests in American geography has been in the function of settlements (Trewartha, 1943, 1952); this has been a growing edge between cultural geography, economics, and other social sciences. An emerging frontier is with medical ecology (public health) on the contacts that man makes with his environment, as revealed in differences in food habits, diets, the deficiency diseases, and disease resistance.

Some Unfulfilled Opportunities for Research

The greatest opportunities for cultural geographers lie in contributing their insights, in cooperation with other geographers and other branches of science, to understanding of the world-wide man-environment system. An essential question for cultural geography is whether its findings return to the system via human society to regulate and control further release of energy or information by the system. To translate this into geographic research problems we need first to consider some of the fundamental questions about the existing cultural pattern of the world and cultural dynamics.

Man as a culture-bearing creature is capable of affecting the course of his own evolution; but what can geographic research contribute toward man's understanding of the effects of his actions upon his own longevity on the earth? We know that biological (organic) evolution produced phenotypes by natural selection, suppressing those genetic traits that were not adapted to conditions of their particular time and place. A biotic process operated over vast periods of time with prodigal elimination, resulting in a rich variety of plants and animals, including man. Culture, involving tools, speech, and cumulative transmittible knowledge, combined with the rapid evolution of man's remarkable cerebral cortex to add a new dimension to evolution. Cultural evolution, a process combining invention and diffusion, is thousands of times faster in effecting changes than is biological evolution.

In the modern period, with the spread over the world of the urban-industrial pattern marked by large per-capita consumption of materials and energy, man's cultural development has reversed the whole trend of evolutionary diversification by reducing (eliminating or absorbing) human diversity in cultures (traditional systems or ways of life) with a trend toward one, great, increasingly complex, interconnecting, specialized system.

A fundamental question is: What does the modern evolutionary trend toward cultural convergence portend for the future of *Homo sapiens?* Does the "putting of many eggs in a single basket" enhance or impair the outlook? Scholars are well aware that the modern near-exponential population growth and the world-wide "revolution of rising expectations" are tending to produce a world of uniform economic orientation. Where, and for what reasons, are the cultural groups which remain less committed to developing and/or maintaining such a uniform world? How successful will they be in maintaining their own identity and existence? What are the relevant spatial elements in their cultures?

Comparative studies are needed of sequences of cultural development in similar natural environments. Is there any evidence that a particular combination of physical and cultural environmental features leads to a given institutional organization in a society? Has the recent establishment of many new nation states in Africa and Asia contributed toward human diversity or been the means of hastening cultural uniformity through dominance of minorities by the political elite (administratively sophisticated, better educated, more numerous)?

Demographers are successfully coping with the problems of counting and locating the increasing numbers of people (natural increase and net migration) as the methods and results of census enumerations have improved, but much more work is needed on determining the amounts and rates of material consumption. Answers are needed not only to "who? and where?" but also to "how much?" and "why?" before reliable comparisons of human qualities of living and of the impact of man upon the world's material resources can be made. For example, much research is needed on food-consumption habits, tolerances, and limits. A common assumption of students of resource-converting techniques has been that if only more food were produced the world could feed itself. But it already is evident that huge surpluses exist in some places that people in other places would not eat (a problem in human values) even if they could be transported elsewhere. What is the nature of these consumption incompatibilities, where are they, and what are their spatial extent and dynamics?

If we are to assume that planned beneficial cultural changes are possible in the world, perhaps the most important research question of all is the study of cultural diffusion processes so as to determine optimal ways of obtaining the spread of beneficial material and non-material innovations.

These broader problems suggest some specific research areas of high social and scholarly significance for cultural geography. Building on the interests, competences, and communications of the recent past, this cluster in geography is in an advantageous position to develop needed knowledge about the space relations of the several major cultures in the world and their values. The focus of its interest could well be on the interaction between culture and the physical-biotic environment. Cultural geography study should be so conducted as to capitalize on its bridge position between physical geography and social anthropology.

Specifically it offers promise for:

(1) Applying modern techniques to studying the nature and rate of diffusion of key culture elements and establishing the evolving spatial pattern of culture complexes.

(2) Measuring cultural effects, and the processes of diffusion that lead to cultural divergences or convergences.

(3) Delineating the critical geographical zones of contact for culture complexes and identifying incipient "hybrids," or conversely discovering "sensitized" areas.

(4) Identifying regions of culture traits (e.g., consumption) incompatible with the traits of the major "aggressive" cultures of today.

(5) Identifying type regions and specific regions where certain cultural values and practices are causing unstable relations between a society and its natural environment.

These opportunities suggest that the subgroup devoted to study of foreign cultures has a key position in the problem area of cultural geography, as does the student of diffusion techniques. Furthermore, the contribution of students in this problem area is likely to have positive value in proportion to their familiarity with social anthropology on the one hand and physical geography on the other. The student committed to research in cultural geography has indeed an exacting study if he seeks the full measure of its potentiality. But thus practiced it has an importance that no perceptive scholar can deny.

3. Studies in Political Geography

The spatial organization of political systems is so distinct and so conspicuous in the spatial pattern of world society that it demands study by special techniques. This has been recognized in geographical research for three-quarters of a century. Political geography's consistent concern with the expression of the sense of territoriality in man makes it one of the foremost keys to the spatial behavior of human society.

Political Systems and Political Space

Every human being lives under, or in contact with, a political system. A majority, perhaps a vast majority, are in touch not only with their own system and its subsystems, but also with one or more outside systems. In an economically advanced section of the world such direct contact commonly concerns several political subsystems, some of them in a hierarchical arrangement. Consider a citizen of certain sections of southern or central California. He may be, and likely is, actively concerned with a school district, an irrigation district, a county, the California state government, and the federal government of the United States. Because he is a citizen of the United States, many political systems impinge upon his life indirectly in alliances like NATO, SEATO, and CENTO, the United Nations, or the governments of individual foreign nations, like India, Taiwan, South Vietnam, or South Africa.

Every political system is prominently, if not preeminently, characterized by geographical area. Indeed, the concept of a nation, and, by extension, the concept of any other political system, is almost unthinkable apart from association with specific territory.[11] The case of the Israeli people through the centuries vividly illustrates this point.

There are thus two inescapable general characteristics of a political system: the political process by or with which it functions, and the terri-

---

[11] Cf. Friedrich Ratzel. "Every state is one part humanity and one part land." (1897, 2.)

tory to which it is bound. Every political process has a geographical area uniquely associated with it and no geographical area escapes some relation with a political process. It is obvious that we are here concerned with one of the most important great subsystems on the face of the planet and one that never can be understood properly without the keenest observation and interpretation of its geographical dimension. It is no accident that the earliest geographical descriptions known referred to political units and that geography throughout most of its long history has rarely been without scholarly attention to the territorial units of political systems.

The modern study of political systems is shared by several subjects. On one hand are political science, sociology, and anthropology, which center their attention upon the social attributes of people and the nature of political process. On the other is political geography, which centers its attention on the part of the earth occupied by a given political system, subsystem, or systems.

Political geography is the study of the interaction of geographical area and political process, or the study of the spatial distribution and space relations of political processes. *Political processes* are defined as the succession of actions or operations which man conducts to establish or to maintain a political system. Most of these processes operate through political institutions, although some are personal or man-institutional group actions.

Although bounded political units are the major focus of area interest, the variable impact of political processes within and beyond the boundaries of a specific political territory also fall within the scope of political geography.

A primary characteristic of political space is its "closed" quality. The territory associated with a political system is not only finite, it is highly specific. The common hunting grounds, the land condominia, and no-man's-land that characterized thousands of years of history on land have been replaced by the border problems of the modern world. These territorial border problems are by no means limited to international boundaries. Indeed, they are probably more numerous for subnational political systems, as exemplified by the problems of the average metropolitan area in the United States today.

Following the concept of Stephen Jones (1954), the "field" of a political system is normally the territory associated with it. In some cases, however, such "fields" extend beyond the territory of the system from which they originate or where they are sustained (e.g., the urbanizing influence of a large industrial and commercial center on surrounding political jurisdictions, or subversive activities inspired by political systems beyond its own borders, etc.). The fields that impinge upon one political system or another are created not only by political processes (expressed in diplomacy or military movement) but also by cultural, economic, and technological phenomena (Ginsburg, 1961).

The "closed" characteristic of political space is especially significant because some important economic functions, ideological and other social forces, and technological forces have space relations that are quite different from those of political processes. It may be said that these forces recognize no political boundaries. Yet they are mobile, sometimes rapid, and penetrating. Their space is a more "open" entity, whose boundaries can advance with astonishing rapidity but also can regress. Indeed, in the demands that the originally non-political processes make upon the internal structure of a given political system or subsystem one discovers some of the most important problems in political geography.

The territorial phenomena of political systems include the: (a) supra-national, (b) national state, (c) domestic-regional political (provinces, states, counties), (d) urban-community or other organized densely settled area, and (e) local or regional special-purpose districts. Each of these territorial entities is associated with a specific political process; together, territory and specific process comprise a political system. The unitary element in the modern world is the political system known as a national state. It is the only entity capable of exercising all the possible political powers or of carrying out all the theoretically possible political processes which bear upon the life of one man or one specific group of men. All the other entities are subsystems, either in the sense of being regional units within the nation-state, special-purpose subsystems within the nation-state, or a regional division thereof (school districts, port authorities, soil conservation districts, development authorities, etc.),[12] or special purpose groupings of national states (military alliances, diplomatic catalyzing organizations like the United Nations, underground organizations for subversion, etc.).

There is one notable part of the earth's surface which is outside all political systems. This is the high seas, which ironically comprise the greater part of the surface of the planet. Viewed somewhat loosely they might be considered a condominium of all nations so situated as to be engaged in either marine or air traffic over them. Considered more carefully the seas have few of the attributes of political space. But the seas are of increasing interest to the nations who use them, and national states are encroaching upon this modern no-man's-land, extending territorial waters for economic and security purposes. On the other hand, air space control has undergone a change in the opposite direction. Orbiting satellites and manned high-altitude flights have changed territorial air space, once responsive to individual political systems, into a new "no man's land."

The Historical Development of Political Geography

The earliest of the modern works on political geography were most concerned with the basic unit, the nation-state, or phenomena associated

---

[12] 18,323 were enumerated by the Census of governments—1962, in the United States. (Urban Survey Corporation, Boston, Massachusetts, 1964.)

with it. Political geographers indeed were among the first scholars to think of the system they were studying in its relation to the total man-natural environment system of the entire earth. They were actively concerned with the dictum stated by Hartshorne that "geography has . . . one, individual, unitary, concrete object of study, namely the whole world." (Hartshorne, 1939, 262)

Because the world does not have a single political organization, and no comprehensively significant body of international law, the earliest memorable studies antecedent to the modern group treat the form and external relations of sovereign states. Thus came the first concerted attention to the subject-theme of political geography: the interaction between a political system in its closed space and political or economic processes kinetically or dynamically associated but not necessarily compatible with the system. Viewed in another way it is the study of the conditions of equilibrium in a political system as they relate to or derive from (a) spatial elements in the system, or (b) the spatial attributes of processes related to the system. The intellectual antecedents of the present cluster in political geography were concerned with the territorial endowments given to existing political systems as they expressed national power.

The first outstanding figure in the field was Friedrich Ratzel of Germany, who first described the state in terms resembling those here suggested. Ratzel even used an analogue model of sorts in presenting his hypothesis of the functioning state as an organism (1897). Ratzel's organic analogue model ("bodenständiger organismus") was accompanied by a detailed methodical analysis of the spatial elements that are part of a national state. Ratzel's work led in two directions: (1) studies and ideological concepts that derived from the organic model, and (2) studies which rejected the model but which perceived the great usefulness of methodical analysis of spatial attributes in the national state as a political system.

The first of these directions included the work of Sir Halford Mackinder (1904, 1919, 1943) who early developed a kinetic spatial model of national power structure. His famous "heartland" and "world island" concepts stressed the dominating potentialities of the Eurasian continent in the political systems of the entire world. The geopolitical school of Germany in 1920-1945 period (Karl Haushofer and his disciples and colleagues, 1934) represented the final flowering of this development and was doomed to extinction because the followers of "geopolitik" departed from scholarly methods. A reflection of geopolitics in the United States was provided for a period during the Second World War and immediately afterward in the works of Nicholas Spykman (1944), Father Edmund Walsh (1948), and a few other non-geographers. Here ended the "geopolitical" line which had commenced with Ratzel's organic state concept.

The second line of study, which derived from Ratzel's methodical study of the spatial conditions of national state existence but which ignored his organic model, commenced when Ellen Semple, a student of Ratzel, came to the University of Chicago (1903). Miss Semple's work (1915) had a historical cast, as did that of Harlan H. Barrows (Koelsch, 1962), whom she influenced in turn. The form of some of her more important work, and that of Barrows, was an analysis of the evolution of a national state within its closed space.

Political Area Studies

a. *The National State.* From these beginnings in the United States two principal problem areas were cultivated. One was a traditional area, that of analyzing the evolution of political units, especially the national state in its historical setting. The state was treated in terms of both its internal and international structure. This approach perhaps reached its best expression in Derwent Whittlesey's "The Earth and the State" (1938). The other major problem area was that of natural resource management.

Because the prevailing methodological concepts of the time denied the possibility of extensive generalization in geography, many of the political area studies are regional descriptions in a historical context. This was true of the main body of Whittlesey's book. In it, however, he speaks of political systems,[13] and "geopolitical forces." Political parties and political movements and "other processes in which laws and regions figure as protagonist and antagonist" are also mentioned by Whittlesey (1938, 589-590).

The hints given by Whittlesey about the importance of studying political processes were examined much more concertedly by Hartshorne (1950), who set a keynote for modern political geography in treating political area differentiation in terms of functional organization. This approach focuses on the politically organized area as a spatial consequence of political process. Refinements were suggested by Gottman (1951, 1952) and Stephen Jones (1954). One essential difference between the older political geography studies and the recent point of view is more complete recognition that political system (political unit) as defined herein and political process do not necessarily cover the same geographical areas. Another difference is emphasis given in more recent studies to the historical and psychological perspectives from which national power is exercised and political behavior explained.

A recent study analyzing blocs of national states from a geographical point of view (Cohen, 1963) stresses the dynamics of geopolitical equilibrium and the complexity of the processes associated with it. The study emphasizes distributional patterns and spatial interactions of peoples and materials who occupy unique political settings, and are oriented to certain channels of movement.

---

[13] "Every political system is the summation of laws which people make in order to extract a livelihood from their habitat." (1938, 577.)

Thus there emerges in recent work of this branch of the field a clear view of significant geographical patterns that are not obscured by focusing exclusively on the political system that is the national state.

b. *Boundaries.* Political area studies have included a number of microgeographical studies, mainly of a systematic nature. A large number of these have treated sections of national boundaries that in some way provide a "window" on the political system that they delimit or the interaction of two or more political systems of which they are an interface. Indeed, boundary study has been one of the most intensively cultivated problem areas of all geography. This is partly because boundaries, like islands, often have a discreteness attractive to the scholar seeking a foothold in a multivariate situation. To identify the frontier zone and its boundary is often easier than to identify the core. Boundary study has also been stimulated by the boundary problems following two world wars and the consequent interest of the United States Department of State. Hartshorne's studies of the Upper Silesian border (1933) and the Polish Corridor (1937), Mackay's (1958) and Minghi's (1963a) studies of the Canada-United States border, and Boggs' (1930) and Pearcy's (1959) studies of maritime boundaries, are illustrative of a great variety of boundary studies on many national areas. Several books that may be considered primary sources of boundary analysis have resulted, including Boggs' study of boundary functions (1940), Jones' handbook (1945), and Alexander's study of northwestern European offshore areas (1963).

c. *Subnational Units.* Boundary studies have in turn led to the study of political systems below the national level of organization, subjects otherwise treated only sparsely in political geography. These include both the domestic-regional and the urban-community. Thus studies by Jones of the Oregon counties (1934), by Ullman of the Rhode Island-Massachusetts boundary (1939), and Nelson on a section of Los Angeles County (1952), again are illustrative. However, such studies have been far fewer than the favored national-international boundary problems, even though a variety of interesting and significant internal boundary problems exist in the United States. Other topics such as electoral geography and the relation between internal physical diversity and political unity have been lightly touched. First treated in terms of counties (Wright, 1932) and provinces (Siegfried, 1950), this area of research is now turning its attention to the interfaces of urban units and political group behavior therein (Lewis, 1958).

Resource Management Studies

The second major problem area in political geography in the United States has rarely been labeled as such, but its origins, content, and conceptual affiliation are nonetheless clear. It is concerned with resource management and land planning in various forms. In contrast with studies of the evolution of political units and the interaction of political area and process, resource management studies have been much more concerned with problems internal to the United States, although a few studies have treated the internal problems of other countries (e.g., White et al, 1962; Ackerman, 1963). One study of economic development covering the world also gives valuable information for resource management investigation (Ginsburg, 1961).

The generalized problem of these studies has been the disequilibrium in a political system caused by nonconformities between land occupance and the existing legal system. Their objective has been the application of spatial analysis to the problems of the *developing* state or political system and to point the way toward equilibria. As Whittlesey noted,

> "To obtain a clear view of the geopolitical forces the earth processes must . . . be studied. Chief among these is the earth's inexorable march from causes to consequences. Laws flagrantly unsuited to regions where they operate ultimately destroy the resource which they govern . . . scarcely any considerable alteration can be performed upon the face of nature without repercussions. Most such operations are possible only to governments." (1938, 589-590.)

The impact of political decisions upon the use of land, be it land occupance for quasi-military purposes as in Israel's frontier areas, or the poiltical organization of Canada's northern territories, this field supplies an almost unending series of problems.

The origins of attention to these studies are easily traced to the early twin interests of Professor Barrows in physical geography and in historical-political geography. He soon developed a conceptual framework for conservation that easily led into the studies of land and water resource planning that Barrows, Colby, White, and others spearheaded in the days of the National Resources Planning Board in the 1930's and early 1940's and that Barrows supervised at the United States Bureau of Reclamation. The peak commitment of geographers to work of this type probably took place in the late 1930's and early 1940's, although a modest flow of geographers into resource planning analysis has continued ever since. A large share of these studies has not been published, but they have contributed to the flow of data and insights that have helped legal and administrative systems in the United States to achieve adjustments to land and other resources. Records of typical activities in the 1930's and 1940's have been left in the publications of the land and water committees of the National Resources Planning Board.

Studies in this problem area have continued since the end of the Second World War consistently on a similar course. They often have been in response to a public need, such as studies for the Natural Resources Task Force of the Commission on the Organization of the Executive Branch (1948), or the President's Water Resources Policy

Commission (1950), and the Senate Select Committee on National Water Resources report (1960).[14] In all these examples an attempt was made to analyze discontinuities between the administrative machinery of the federal political system of the United States and the spatial phenomena to which they are related. An attempt was made to codify the "normal" situation for these relations in the light of modern technology by Ackerman and Löf (1959). Interesting social and psychological elements in resource management were brought out by White and his colleagues in their flood plain studies (White, 1958).

An example of the study undertaken on a state level is that by the Maryland State Department of Planning (1961). That study caused a reorganization of Maryland state resource development agencies to a structure more responsive to regional problems than it had been (e.g., management of the tidewater areas). As before the war, study not leading to formal publication again has formed an important part of scholarly activity in this area. An example was the formulation of concepts which led eventually to the establishment of the Delaware River Basin Commission in Eastern United States, an experiment in combined federal-state management of an important resource in a heavily settled region.

The principal research on political geography by United States students in recent years therefore has been divided into two main problem areas: the study of political areas, and especially their interfaces, and the study of domestic resource management and land planning problems. Both of these are special cases within the subject theme described earlier: study of the conditions of equilibrium in a political system as they relate to or derive from spatial elements in the system, or the spatial attributes of processes related to the system. The study of boundaries is essentially the study of interfaces between political systems. The study of resource management and planning essentially has been the study of spatial organization in the giant state. Viewed thus, we shall see that these research interests have a high degree of significance for future work in political geography.

Relations with Other Fields

Political geography can make a valid contribution to geography only by dealing with political process. This involves a working relation with other fields, particularly political science and history. Historically, political geography has had its closest contact with political science through the study of international relations. Indeed, the late 19th and early 20th century inquiry into the relationship between the political power of nations and the earth-man environment by geographers like Ritter, Guyot, Ratzel, Mackinder, was grasped by political scientists as a new realistic basis for analyzing the relation among states.

---

[14] The not yet completed studies of the Alaskan Earthquake Committee of the National Academy of Sciences-National Research Council belong to this group.

"International Relations—essentially a series of approaches to interpret and systematize the various forces and factors that have characterized the relations among states . . . owes its emergency to the down-to-earth realism of 19th century geographers." (Gyorgy, 1963)

Interdisciplinary communication in recent years, however, has been sporadic at best. Because of this and early emphasis on the foundations of national power by geographers, many political scientists misconceive geography as consisting of a number of variables of the physical environment (Fitzsimmons, 1957). Singer (1960) speaks of "geographical variables which are only partially, if at all, subject to human modification." In the several articles contributed by political scientists to a survey of geography and international conflict ("Geography of Conflict," *Journal of Conflict Resolution,* 1960) there is almost no reference to or recognition of contemporary geographical literature or thought. Yet some subjects of great significance to politics, like voting behavior and legislative redistricting, can be examined completely only with the aid of modern geographic techniques.

On the other hand, new methods and concepts in political scientists' study of political process are useful and should be attractive to geographers concerned with the study of boundaries and other spatial phenomena on the interfaces of political systems. Kirk (1951) and the Sprouts (1956) were among the first to introduce behaviorism and decision-making theories to geographers. Works such as those of Deutsch on social complementarity (1953) and measuring the political community (1954), German's study of the application of national power, using national psychological and sociological intangibles to weigh and modify natural and human resources (1960), Koch's matrix analysis to indicate interaction between geographical variables and institutions and motivations (1960), and Schelling's application of game theory to political process (1960) are worth exploring as avenues of joint research for geographers and political scientists. At the same time, game theory and decision-making studies of state behavior are being made with inadequate reference to global geopolitical equilibrium theories.

For those students of political geography who have been most concerned with resource management and other aspects of spatial organization in a giant state, decision-making in both its economic and political aspects also is an important related field of study, particularly the slowly reviving field of political economy. Hirshman's (1963) research in political economics, such as his discussion of the role that political motivation played in leading to the multipurpose São Francisco development project, is an example of a study of process that has significance for geographical research. Study of the role of public policy and of personal motivation in the management and use of land resources (Clawson, Held, and Stoddard, 1960) illustrates another closely related approach. The outmoding of county units, the consequences of the establishment of new administrative districts, and the retention of regional myths in national politics are other examples of topics dealt with by related fields that are pertinent to political geography. Jones (1961) suggested that the study of administrative areas could be an attractive meeting ground for political scientists and political geographers.

There would seem to be a particularly rich source of collaborative interest with other social scientists now studying urban affairs, including sociologists, economists, and political scientists. Urban political and social motivational studies (Levin and Blackwood, 1962) and urban economics (Perloff, Wingo et al., 1961)—including public expenditures policies, manpower-budget, cost-benefit analyses and highway-impact studies—all contribute data that are extremely useful, if not vital, to the student of political spatial organization on a local scale. They are as yet very incompletely exploited by geographers. The interfaces between local political systems offer some of the most interesting materials for the future because of the rapidity of urbanization in the United States and many other countries. The clash between closed urban political space and the total earth-man urbanized system closely parallels the clash on the national-state-international level, warranting much more cross-field investigation than has been applied to date.

Unfulfilled Opportunities

With only a handful of practitioners in a field of vast potential scope, and they, sharply divided into two groups with only a moderate frequency of communication obviously cultivating a field which calls for close interdisciplinary attention and not yet having fully developed it, the problems of research in political geography are many. But the opportunities are many also and of the highest social significance.

In a world where high policy from politically sophisticated powerful nations can produce political-geographic monstrosities like the boundary between North and South Korea, the Berlin exclave, and the quadripartite division of former French Indochina, the need for professional study of political geography of international interfaces by students of the highest competence can only be described as urgent.

A need for studying the territorial viability of small states is also urgent. The break-up of the Colonial system has seen the number of independent states grow from 71, on the eve of the Second World War, to 125 today. This proliferation of nations has created serious international complications by introducing many small, weak, and poor national states into the world system. More than 60 nations have less than 5 million inhabitants each and 31 less than 2 million each. These small countries make every effort to maintain their economic and political postures as equals within the international community. Yet the role that such states can realistically hope to play in world affairs is a function of their territorial viability. It is a problem area that very seriously merits the attention of political geographers.

The need for equally competent study of political geography on an intranational scale, while not equally urgent, must also be considered pressing. Nations' populations are growing in total numbers with a rapidity never before equaled in history, concentrating those numbers in limited areas with unprecedentedly high densities, superimposing those masses of people on spatially organized political systems devised for relatively sparse or uniformly spread settlement, and at the same time coping with new and revolutionary technology. It is not surprising that disequilibria within the large national states, and particularly the United States, are the rule rather than the exception. The racial and urban-rural frictions today threatening the society of the United States undoubtedly have some of their causes in these spatial disequilibria, now poorly understood and little mentioned.

In the face of the formidable array of problems which the two clusters in political geography can treat, the important questions would seem to be those of future training of students of political area or resource management, enhanced communication both within geography and between geography and other fields, and the most strategic deployment of the limited research potential likely to be available. Stated in another manner, how can past tradition in these studies and present capacities of research workers in the two clusters of interest be capitalized on, and how are the research frontiers of the field to be developed?

To reach some conclusions as to how political geography may contribute with increasing effectiveness to research on political systems in the world, several background observations seem pertinent.

(1) Political geography problems are essentially interdisciplinary. That is, the most effective research and most meaningful answers result when methods and data from two or more traditional scholarly fields, including geography, are applied in research. In studying political area organization as the spatial consequence of political process, there are important questions on ideological concepts, individual and group behavior, rates of political maturation, degree of applicability or resistance to political laws, and diffusion of ideas that go far beyond the accustomed competence of the individual geographer. International relations, economics, sociology and social psychology, may in turn be absolutely essential to the understanding of specific problems in political geography. Determination of a research problem within its full system context is an essential step.

(2) Communication between geographers and political scientists and other social scientists has been sporadic and largely ad hoc, related to a specific and temporary research interest. The cultivation of an effective jointly based discipline, like biophysics or biochemistry, which could and should be a goal, thus has had little stimulus. If there is to be such a joint effort, the unit area framework used by political geographers is a window that can be valuable to political and social scientists in their concern with intra-state processes.

(3) Political geographers have been accustomed to thinking in terms of systems and system relationships almost from the beginning of their field (cf. Ratzel). Thus a system framework mentioned elsewhere in this report will be easily understood by the political geographer, and his work easily adapted to it. Indeed, at least a few efforts toward treating the specific problems on a systems scale have appeared in the recent past (Ackerman and Löf, 1959). However, nearly all political geography thought has been empirically oriented. Thus far it has had little relation to formal systems theory. The dialogue between the empirical and the theoretical has not been habitual. At the same time it is now obvious that at least some aspects of systems theory, like theories of diffusion, are fundamental to the study of political geography problems.

(4) No single group of political geography research workers exists at the present time. Instead there are the two clusters described elsewhere in this report. One is the group which has studied political areas, especially their interface problems within political systems, most often on an international plane—the successors to the older geographers interested in the evolution of the national state. The second is the group which has paid particular attention to the spatial organization of resource management in our political system. The general problem that this latter group is concerned with is the internal spatial organization of the giant state, whether it is federal or other.

This Committee believes that students of political geography, in spite of their small number, have contributed effectively and consistently in the recent past to two research frontiers. These are in boundary studies, and in the spatial organization of resource management and planning. It is now reasonable to inquire as to whether either one or both of these does constitute a research frontier. They should be judged both from the point of view of social significance and from the point of view of intellectual significance.

The Committee agrees that the case for social significance needs little argument. Every reader of a newspaper, from his repeated exposure to Berlin and Korea, and more recently to Southeast Asia, knows that there are international boundary problems even though he may not recognize them under such a classification. The sensitive interfaces between the two great international political systems are in themselves sufficient reason for competent professional study in this area. However, study of the interfaces between political systems should anticipate boundary and other problems; they should anticipate spatial causes of friction and barriers to interchange. The creation of more than 50 new nations within the last 20 years, many having boundaries that are relicts of colonial times, suggests that boundary tensions in Africa and Asia are very likely to remain as breeders of local wars for decades to come. Furthermore, the appearance of a totally new type of boundary, the Iron Curtain type, is a further challenge to study.

Indeed, boundaries of the world may be classified today into two general types: (a) The Iron Curtain type, curiously open to the export of political process and military means, but much more impervious to economic traffic and nearly opaque to social movement and to the import of political process. (b) The Western type of political boundary, increasingly open to economic movement, relatively open to social movement, somewhat less opaque to the import of political process than the Iron Curtain, and relatively closed to the export of political process. There are undoubtedly many variations of these general types which, fully understood, have much practical significance in future international relations.

Studies of internal boundaries and the studies of the spatial organization of resource management and planning are also considered by the Committee to have a high degree of social significance. Both of the giant national states of today, the United States and the Soviet Union, have shown increasingly visible stresses in the last 10 years because of the internal spatial organization of their political systems, different as they are. The European Common Market grouping is just reaching a stage where these internal stresses may be even more sharply outlined. Geographic studies are needed to complement the new interest in study of political economy that has developed since 1945. International river basins, like the Mekong, the Jordan, the Indus, the Nile, and others, are also centers of stress, although they also can be viewed as potential bases for international accord.

It would thus seem difficult to choose two problem areas which have a higher social significance than these at the present time.

There remains a need to comment briefly on the intellectual significance of these two general subjects. Here again they appear to answer the tests for significance. They offer relatively discrete subjects; local problems may be chosen so as to give insights on the larger national political system or the interactions thereof with another system; both would seem to be attractive to an experimenter with the application of formal systems analysis; and both unquestionably have the study of geographical space prominent in needs for solution and understanding.

Lying beyond these immediately approachable subjects are others of great significance which may be susceptible to geographic analysis. For example, what is a small state and what is state viability? Must the geopolitical structure of the recently emerged small state conform to that of the larger traditional national state to afford viability? How does the proliferation of small states affect the geopolitical foundations of the United Nations, which was not structured to cope with such numbers?

In another vein, how are the attitudes of people toward the great ideologies (communism, socialism, nationalism, economic *laissez-faire*, etc.) spatially distributed and diffused in particular countries, and over the earth? What are the spatial parameters of different attitudes toward a minority group, and what are their dynamics? Voting behavior, a subject that is being examined in increasingly fine detail, has geographical components. What are they; and how significant are they? What is the geography of demagogic control?

We believe that these and other serious problems facing the world could receive helpful illumination by competent geographic study.

4. Location Theory Studies

Several traditional subfields of geography, including economic, urban, and transportation geography, are not discussed in this report as problem areas as they once might have been, because their status is unclear today. Recent development in all three traditional subjects has involved extensive application of mathematical methods to facilitate refinement of theory, and a higher level of generalization than existed before has emerged. As a result, it would appear that the three traditional fields have been joined in a problem area which we here entitle, for want of another name, location theory studies. It is of special interest in our discussion because these studies include: (a) research on the qualities of space in a theoretical framework; (b) application of formal systems methods to space relations study; and (c) integration of at least three of the spatial subsystems of culture. In location theory studies the "dialogue" between the empirical and the theoretical has gone farthest, revealing the potential power of a balanced approach when applied to other geographical problem areas. It is also of interest for the extent to which its methods and concepts have found practical applications in a revitalized "applied geography" directed publicly to problems of urban and regional planning, and privately to marketing analysis for plant and store location.

Characteristics of the Problem Area, and the Research Cluster

The development, testing, and refinement of location theory, related studies of the geographic organization of economic life, and of urban and transportation systems, have been fundamental to the work of geographers interested in this problem area. The applicable body of theory includes, on the one hand, abstract concepts concerning spatial distributions and space relations and, on the other hand, more substantive formulations focused particularly upon the economic, urban, and transportation aspects of geography. Indeed, the cluster of research interest in this area evolved after the Second World War within the framework of economic geography, urban geography, and transportation geography. Very recently a new synthesis has begun to emerge based upon: (1) the identity of spatial concepts and principles developed in these and other subfields of geography; and (2) emphasis upon the interaction of economic, urban, and transportation phenomena in interdependent regional systems that are the material consequences of man's resource-converting and space-adjusting techniques. This emerging synthesis thus results from a concerted application of systems theory within geography. Each of these points is exemplified below (see "Hierarchy of Problems").

Empirical work of members of the cluster is characteristically analytic; questions are usually resolved by reducing them to equations. This "quantitative bias" reflects concern for more rigorous hypothesis testing, interest in statistical regularities that are the basis of theoretical speculation, and desire to delve explicitly into the functioning of spatial processes. In addition the bias reflects a deliberate choice by location theory students to participate in the intensified quantitative activity that has affected all sciences since the Second World War. Thus the techniques differentiating members of the cluster from more traditional geographers are the same techniques that differentiate the more from the less quantitatively inclined in other subjects: inferential statistics; modern mathematics, including linear algebra; set theory and the theory of graphs; programming techniques and simulation procedures (Garrison, 1965).

Location theory studies are best developed in American geography (Garrison, 1960; Berry, 1965). However, wherever a similar combination of theoretical orientation, mathematization, and systems-theoretic thinking has been applied to the study of spatial distributions and space relations, a similar community of interest has emerged. Among the instances of independent invention are: (a) a Swedish group, centered on the Royal University of Lund (Hägerstrand, 1953; Kulldorf, 1956); (b) a Finnish group, particularly at the University of Helsinki (Ajo, 1962; Palomaki, 1963); (c) a Polish group, focused in the Polish Academy of Sciences in Warsaw (Wrobel, 1960); and (d) more recent stirrings in France (Claval, 1962). Formal recognition was given to the cluster by the International Geographical Union in the summer of 1964, when it established a Commission on Quantitative Methods in Geography, with six full members who are leading practitioners in the field: Garrison (U.S.A., Chairman), Hägerstrand (Sweden), Saushkin (U.S.S.R.), Chorley (U.K.), Mabogunje (Nigeria), and Prakasa Rao (India), plus corresponding members reflecting the range of current activity.

Hierarchy of Problems

The problems studied by the geographers in this group can best be summarized in the form of a hierarchy of elemental and field theories and working hypotheses that is being assembled. As with all hierarchies, the one presented here is built such that each higher level is more general than each of the preceding lower levels in the questions that it asks.

At the initial level of the hierarchy are studies of the structure of spatial distributions of phenomena at varying scales and therefore positions along the regional-topical continuum. Studies of spatial structure emphasize such static aspects of pattern as location, spread, density and geometry. A second step is to consider actual linkages and flows between places as they are expressed in terms of various phenomena. Studies of spatial systems or functional organization emphasize these linkages, using such themes as accessibility, connectivity, dominance and hierarchy in addition to the location and geometry of the connections themselves. A third level of generalization is to be found in the temporal dynamics of spatial structure and spatial systems. Studies of change through time might involve comparative statics, process, and the idea of equilibrium, either deterministic or stochastic. A final level is represented by the use of normative models. Rather than studying *what* the systems are and *why* they are, they could be discussed at the normative level of what *should* be if the goals were x and the constraints on the achievement of these goals were y and z, thereby deriving efficiency solutions.

Berry (1964a) provides the basis for an illustration of these levels in the form of a regional-topical data matrix. The matrix itself represents one point in time. Each row represents a topic variable; each column a place. Spatial structure is shown by scalar values in cells, representing geographic facts, or the values of variables at particular places and times. Spatial systems could be shown by a vector in each cell representing flow of a particular variable between a particular place and other places. To show dynamics of spatial structure and spatial systems, a succession of matrices containing scalar and vector values could be constructed for different points in time. Finally, a set of goals, costs and constraints could be developed and the matrix solved for minimum-cost or maximum welfare so as to provide an efficiency solution.

a. *Studies of Spatial Structure.* Study of spatial structure has proceeded in a variety of ways. Several separate lines of inquiry have converged to show systematic patterning of spatially distributed data. For example, the many census variables which are collected decennially to characterize different areas within cities consistently degenerate to just three underlying patterns, indicative of differences in socio-economic rank, stage of families in the life cycle, and segregation of ethnic minorities (Berry, 1964b). Similar studies show degeneration of many variables used to study economic development to only a few patterns (Berry, 1961; Ray and Berry, 1965). Population densities within central cities drop consistently in a negative exponential manner with distance from the city center, the rate of decline bearing a consistent, predictable relationship to city size (Berry, Simmons and Tennant, 1963). Land values within cities obey similar rules (Knos, 1962). Many social, economic, and cultural phenomena show significant distance-decay relationships with increasing distance from cities (Ajo, 1963; Stewart and Warntz, 1958; Taaffe, Garner and Yeates, 1963). Later stages in an industrial production sequence are less likely to be centralized in the American manufacturing belt than are earlier stages (McCarty *et al.*, 1956).

Theories have now been formulated to account for such systematic patterning of most of the elements making up larger spatial systems: agricultural and urban land use; industrial location; location of retail and service trade; urban location; and the layout of transport networks. Chisholm (1962), for example, summarizes the classic agricultural location theory of J. H. Von Thünen and the more recent work of W. Isard, E. Dunn, and others, and amasses much empirical material to verify the main postulates of the theory at a variety of scales, from primitive village to agriculture in world trade. These postulates involve systematic decreases in intensity of agricultural land use and concomitant changes in the nature of that use as costs of shipping products to market rise with increasing distance from markets, subject to discontinuities caused by differentials in resource endowment. Garrison and Marble (1957) offer proof for the theorem that for every location there exists an optimum intensity of production and combination of crops. Alonso (1963) extends this work to land use within cities making use of the foundation laid by R. M. Haig in studies of New York during the 1920's (1927; see also Borchert, 1961). Estall and Buchanan (1961) provide a similar summary and exemplification of Weber's classical and Isard's more recent contributions to industrial location theory. Claval (1962) summarizes relevant studies of marketing. However, the general statement of retail location is provided by the central place theory of W. Christaller and related contributions by A. Lösch. The latter theory and a massive body of related empirical work is reviewed by Berry and Pred (1961). The major postulate is that retail activities locate in a hierarchy of market centers distributed spatially in a regular tessellation; centers at each successively higher level of the hierarchy perform all functions of the lower levels plus a larger-scale group necessarily provided to larger service areas from fewer, more widely spaced locations. Central place theory thus provides a statement not only of retail, but also of urban, location (see also Curry, 1963; Morrill, 1963; Palomaki, 1963; Thomas, 1960, 1962).

b. *Studies of Spatial Systems or Functional Organization.* A second level of studies focuses on linkages between places in terms of various phenomena and thus upon the map in which different structural elements fit together in interacting, interdependent spatial systems. Central place theory, therefore, tells not only about locational patterns of retailing and of market towns of different rank; it also relates how the size and spacing of centers of each rank are intertwined with each other, with the market areas served, and with consumer travel behavior (Berry, 1964b). Flows of goods, people, and information have often been used to study the functional organization of areas in systems of nodal regions (Nystuen and Dacey, 1961). Transport networks have been analyzed with the intent of measuring accessibility of places to the network, and degree of connectivity of the whole (Garrison and Marble, 1962; Kansky, 1963).

The generalization which has received most attention as a description of movements is the gravity model—that movements between areas are in direct proportion to the products of the masses and inversely proportional to distance separating the areas raised to an exponent (Carrothers, 1958). A related model is that of population potentials, which summarizes the accessibility of each element to the whole, and which has been argued to be highly correlated with many other descriptive variables of a social and economic kind in the United States (Stewart and Warntz, 1958; Warntz, 1959; Borchert, 1961). Each of these formulations emphasizes the focal role of urban centers in the organization of spatial systems, and some also tie an understanding of transport networks into the analysis of spatial distributions and space relations. Unfortunately, an adequate theoretical base has not been provided as yet for either of these models.

c. *Simple Studies of Dynamics in Spatial Systems.* At the third level, that of simple dynamics, contributions are fewer and the present rate of development is slower. Two approaches to the study of process can be distinguished, both containing the concept of equilibrium: (a) simple deterministic analysis, and (b) analysis utilizing stochastic processes. The first case involves a simple extension of ideas of structure and of functional organization: given a spatial system in equilibrium, what will be the flow of effects if one element or one connection is changed? Simpler studies have used comparative statics to show how various things change together through time. For example, Berry, Simmons and Tennant (1963) showed how changes in the population density gradient of cities through time were the same as changes in the gradient with increasing city size. Kansky (1963) showed how changes in transport network structure with changes in economic development were the same as changes in structure with differences in level of economic development for a cross-section of countries today.

Perhaps the best examples of the simpler kinds of dynamic study by analytically minded geographers have been in the field of highway network analysis and synthesis answering the question, "What have been the effects upon land uses, households, and business firms of constructing highway X?" Examples are Garrison's (1956) study of highway benefits in the State of Washington, and Borchert's study of the Minneapolis-St. Paul area (1961). See also the Garrison-Marts (1958) summary. These studies were undertaken as part of the federal government's attempts to codify, measure, and place a monetary value on the indirect effects of new highway construction. Garrison's argument was that reductions in transport costs accrue directly as increases in land values. A similar study by Berry (1963) is designed to "lay out the extent, location, nature and causes of commercial deterioration and blight in Chicago."

The second case, that of stochastic equilibrium systems, was first approached by Hägerstrand of Sweden in studies of the cityward migration of rural people and of the diffusion of innovations into rural areas from centers of innovation (Hägerstrand, 1953), He found that the long-run effects of such spatial processes could be summarized in terms of probability distributions that are the outcome of probabilistic growth (stochastic) processes. Further, knowing the points of origin and the rules for growth based upon diminishing probabilities of interaction with increasing distance separating origins and destinations, he found that he was able to simulate the spatial diffusion process. Hägerstrand's work has stimulated a good deal of interest among American members of the location theory cluster, leading not only to migration and innovation studies, but also to examinations of such other spatial processes as the journey-to-work (Taaffe, 1963) and the development of systems of cities and their transport connections (Morrill, 1963; Curry, 1964; Berry, 1964b). Recent attention has also been addressed to use of simulation models as means of evaluating alternative city planning policies, providing the geographer and urban planner with an opportunity to conduct laboratory-type research into the phenomena with which they deal under conditions of uncertainty (Garrison, 1962).

d. *Efficiency Solutions.* In addition to the scientific study of spatial systems as they exist, efficiency studies have also been pursued. These investigations involve, first, the development of manipulable models descriptive of the system and, second, analysis to determine the form of the system if the models are made to maximize or minimize some function subject to constraints. One early attempt along these lines is the Garrison-Marble (1958) linear programming formulation of highway network to find the land-use system, rent levels, and transport network that would satisfy certain goals. An excellent example of what is possible with a spatial programming approach was recently provided by Heady (1964). A related type of study uses spatial price equilibrium analysis, designed to obtain optimal price levels and trade flows to achieve sets of production and consumption goals. Examples are the Morrill-Garrison (1959) study of trade in wheat and flour or the Chuang-Judge (1964) studies of the United States animal feed economy. Another use of the normative model is to contrast its implications with that of an analytic model. Wolpert (1964) attempts to explain, for example, why the farming system of Sweden does *not* conform to an efficiency solution, the reasons including conflicts in goals, lags in communication, variations in perception, etc.

Efficiency-type contributions are fewer in number than those of other kinds, but this should be less true in the future as theory becomes sufficiently articulate and explicit, and better geographic data banks are organized. The two most difficult tasks in such an approach remain in the formulation of the model, and the assembly of adequate relevant data. At present, the most active work with spatial programming is in the fields of agricultural production patterns, and metropolitan land use. In the latter case it is being used as an alternative to simulation procedures in improving decision-making among urban and transportation planners (Lowry, 1964).

Relations with Other Subjects

Relations with other subjects have been critical in the development of the location theory cluster and its analytic interests. The growing concern with theory and the spread of quantification which has characterized recent developments in social science has been reflected in the work of this group in part because of its contact with other subjects. Mathematics and statistical methods, rather than acting as a barrier, have served as a common language which has facilitated communications with other subjects despite other semantic barriers.

Economics and sociology are the two academic fields most closely related to the cluster. In both of these subjects, the post-war period has seen a growth of interest in the spatial expression of phenomena. The economics of location, urban, agricultural, transport, and regional economics, and international trade theory treat some of the same concepts considered in studies of spatial structure, organization, and processes, the first three levels of theoretical inquiry. The work of many demographers and human ecologists, particularly that relating to metropolitan regions, has been quite close to that of urban geographers. The work of the location theory cluster has also been carried into application through planning at a variety of levels. In addition to the routine, local-level problems of land use and transportation, urban renewal, and the like that have been treated by geographers for some time (Berry, 1963) and such long-term geographic concerns with problems of area delineation as are reflected in the status of the Geography Division of the Census Bureau, developmental problems with broad implications for different categories of planners are now being approached to mutual advantage. Highway network analyses are related to the work of the transportation and regional planner (Garrison and Marble, 1957, 1962). Studies of spatial organization, for example those of economic regionalization, are of interest to both the city and regional planner (Wrobel, 1960). Geographers are designing the data bank for the Canada Land Inventory which will be an integral part of the program of that country's Agricultural Rehabilitation and Development Agency, and are working with the Office of Regional Economics of the United States Department of Commerce.

A common meeting ground has been in "regional science" and communication has been much facilitated by an interdisciplinary group known as the Regional Science Association, which has regional economists, other economists, geographers, human ecologists, city planners, regional planners, and other specialists among its members. In many respects, members of this group have worked with the same substantive data as have economic, urban, and transportation geographers, but from a more abstract point of view. As the abstractions were discussed, their relevance to empirical study became apparent. Geographers interested in the problems began to acquaint themselves with the theory and methods employed by the regional economists and vice versa, and both benefited. At present, geographers rank with economists as comprising the largest share of the membership of the Association.

Unfulfilled Opportunities

A major opportunity seen by workers in the location theory problem area is that of integrating their work more closely with other geographers as they begin to deal with spatial systems of political, cultural, and physical phenomena. In the future, analysis of spatial systems should be conceived more broadly to encompass a wider range of concepts and embrace a wider range of phenomena. This could be achieved in three different ways: (1) by an intensification of activity and communication within the cluster; (2) by better communication between members of the cluster and workers in other disciplines such as economics and sociology; (3) by the accelerated diffusion of techniques and concepts to other geographers, and communication on the definition of research problems. The result would be to hasten the confrontation of empirical-inductive studies by theoretical-deductive approaches throughout geography.

There is some evidence to suggest that each of these three ways can be followed in a manner which is practical. Under the sponsorship of the National Science Foundation, several introductory institutes organized by members of the cluster have apparently served to accelerate growth of the cluster substantially, by enabling more geographers to read the literature, to guide their graduate training programs more effectively, and to introduce significant research findings into undergraduate teaching. Similarly, advanced conferences sponsored by the National Science Foundation and by the Geography Branch of the Office of Naval Research have enabled interested geographers to delve more deeply into work of the cluster, and to launch themselves into theoretical-quantitative geographic analysis. Topics of such conferences include the use of computers in geographic research, and statistical analysis of spatial distributions.

A major unfulfilled opportunity lies in accelerated diffusion of techniques and concepts from members of the cluster to other geographers and the "feedback" this diffusion always generates in terms of questions to be answered. This is a matter of particular importance to geography because of the large research potential represented by regional and other geographers whose knowledge of specific areas and specific spatial distributions could effectively be combined with an awareness of theoretical concepts to produce useful studies of greater generality. Testing of theory in a variety of empirical contexts should aid in the overall development and refinement of viable theories. It should also serve to connect geographic progress to local problems more rapidly and more effectively.

It is also critical that the accelerating rate of progress within the cluster be maintained, and certain immediate opportunities and problems are apparent. A large arena for substantive progress appears to be accessible in the development of simulation and efficiency models of dynamic spatial systems. In the past this has been limited by technical considerations. Yet the cluster has barely kept abreast of continuing technological change, particularly the newer and larger computers, mainly because of a shortage of effective manpower. It is now possible to develop large central data banks which can be available on call. For example, the United States Housing and Home Finance Agency has supported much recent research into the development of general-purpose metropolitan data banks. Reference has already been made to the Canada Land Inventory. For geographers to benefit further from these data systems it is important that they be able to structure them so that the stored data can be assigned locational as well as other referencing codes. But research is needed as to the nature of proper locational coding, and this must be accomplished before structuring can be accomplished. (Geographic Coding Subcommittee, 1960; Kao, 1963).

We now stand on the verge of developing man-machine systems such that concepts can immediately be referred to a computer system and a data bank for testing and results. Such man-machine interaction should have dramatic effects upon the research process and should also affect transmission of ideas in the classroom. Given a machine system that can store a dynamic model of a city, geographers could see the results of alternative land use, highway location, or development planning policies, receiving as output from the machine cartographic and graphic displays, tabular materials, and relevant descriptive parameters for the system's equations. Both teaching and planning, as well as research, could thus be made more effective. These steps are on the threshold of attainment, yet they will require a far greater investment in facilities even in the current state of the computer art than has ever before been demanded by geography. Without such investment the opportunities will be lost. Present investment needs are likely to be compounded, for we also stand on the verge of dramatic changes in the means of data input to and output from data banks attached to central computers. Initial exploration is already in progress into automated scanning of maps for immediate digitizing of inputs, into the geographic uses of observations from outer space, remote sensing of environment, and "real time" observation of transport systems. When developed they will provide opportunities for direct observation of systems under study, and hence the potentiality for more effective control and for experimentation via observation of feedback mechanisms. Similarly, automation of cartography through plotter and electronic cathode-ray devices will provide greater flexibility for study and analysis, hasten the confrontation between hypothesis and evidence, and allow the research worker the rapid reformulation and precision of thought needed for continuous problem refinement. Again, most of the research and the "hardware design" needs to be completed.

If these opportunities are lost, some very significant support for the space-management arts also will be lost. The most effective allocation of multi-billion-dollar land-use and resource management investments literally hangs on the type of information which location theory and other geographic studies can make available.

What are the constraints to satisfactory exploitation of technical aids? An inadequate supply of properly trained manpower is the most serious present limitation. A significant increase must be made in the number of effective workers in the cluster if the research opportunities provided by technological change are to be translated into continued progress. Technical research and development will be inadequate in volume and scope as long as the present critical manpower shortage continues. Finally, there must be adequate manpower in the cluster if it is to achieve effective diffusion of research findings and experimental possibilities to other research geographers. Viewed broadly, the foremost research need of the cluster is therefore a training need.

III. Conclusions and Recommendations

Limitations in Scope of Report

The Committee has not attempted complete coverage of the field of geography in the foregoing survey. Geographers will readily recognize that some familiar subjects of the past, including studies of agriculture, population, and regional geography are not included, except by reference. Yet of eight "processes" that had been postulated as important in the study of space relations (Ackerman, 1958, 22-26), all have been referred to in the above descriptions. It will be recalled that four of these processes are "natural": movement of the unconsolidated part of the earth's crust, movement of water over land, climatic processes, and biotic processes. Four cultural processes also were included: the habits of man as a cultural-demographic unit, the evolution of political and administrative organization, and the resource-converting and space-adjusting techniques. In the comments which follow, therefore, the Committee feels warranted in speaking about geography as a whole, even though its cluster descriptions were selective. The succeeding statements are organized to answer directly the questions put to the Committee by Dr. M. King Hubbert in his letter of invitation to the Committee (pp. viii-ix). They are given below under three headings: (1) The potential contributions of geography to the progress of science and society, (2) a strategy of research in geography, and (3) catalytic actions for implementation of the strategy.

Potential Contributions of Geography to the Progress of Science and Society

The Committee set forth four premises at the outset of this report: (a) Scientific progress and social progress are closely correlated if not equated. (b) Full understanding of the world-wide system comprising man and his natural environment is one of the four or five great overriding problems in all science. (c) The social need for knowledge of space relations of man and natural environment rises, rather than declines, as the world becomes more settled and more complex, and may

54

reach a crisis stage in the near future. (d) Progress in any branch of science concerns all branches, because science as a whole is epigenetic.

Geography and the Progress of Science

If it may be assumed that understanding of the world-wide system comprising man and his natural environment is one of the great over-riding problems of all science, it then remains to restate how geography contributes effectively toward this understanding.

As it examines research problems related to this overriding problem, geography is concerned primarily with space in time. Geography seeks to explain how the subsystems of the physical world are organized on the earth's surface, and how man distributes himself over the earth in his space relation to physical features and to other men. Space and space relations compose one of the great mediators of the characteristics of any part of the system at any point on the earth's surface. Because it is one of the major subjects concerned with spatial features on the earth's surface, and because it is the only one traditionally concerned with system interrelations within the space of the earth's surface, we conclude that geography does have a significant place in satisfying man's scientific curiosity.

The position of geography is particularly interesting at this time because it is a "bridge" position. Partly as a result of a tenacious legacy from the Middle Ages and partly for practicality and expediency the research works of science have divided themselves between the natural and the social (human). Among all the sciences geography is one of the few that has been consistently concerned with phenomena in both the natural and social areas. In view of the growing recognition that no phenomenon on the earth's surface can be treated independently, the Committee suggests that this aspect of geography's past habits of thought has prepared it well for approaching some scientific problems of the present day.

Finally, all geography has had a firm tradition of field observation, an important aspect of its past empirical-inductive bias. This tradition may have been emphasized to a fault in the past, for little geographical research was considered professionally acceptable unless it was based on field observation. With the exception of anthropology, the field-observation tradition has been stronger than in any other subject treating cultural phenomena. Now that the barrier of generalization in a formal systems context has been crossed, geography's tradition for field study places it in an excellent position for testing any generalization or any theoretical construct against primary sources. The division of labor between the geographical field student and the location theoretician is not unlike the symbiotic relation between astrophysics and observational astronomy that has contributed so strikingly to our knowledge of the universe. For geography, however, the relation of field observation and theory is still in a relatively early stage. The Committee believes, nevertheless, that it offers a powerful intellectual combination that should be fostered.

Potential Geographical Contributions to the Understanding of Social Problems

The Committee also believes that there are excellent social reasons for improving the status of geographic research and increasing its effort. We should like to call attention to the following:

(1) The growth of men's numbers has advanced with startling rapidity in this century. There has been an exponential growth of the world's population in 50 years. The next doubling is expected to occur within 40 years, with an ever-shorter doubling period in prospect. President Seitz of the National Academy of Sciences has stated, "The problem of uncontrolled population growth emerges as one of the most critical issues of our time. . . ." (Natl. Acad. Sci., 1963). Hubbert has shown that materials and energy production cannot continue to increase exponentially also, and that "the dominant limiting factors become land area and food supply." (Hubbert, 1964, 60). Problems of land area are problems of space relations.

(2) Technology, paced by science, has gathered momentum at an astonishing rate within this century. The impact of man on the earth has been so profound in the last half century, and especially in the last two decades, that no biotic study and no study of the surface features of the earth can proceed without reckoning these effects. Improvement in transportation technique and penetration particularly has increased interdependence and interaction, the distinguishing features of all systems. The study of transportation requires space relations analysis.

(3) On a world-wide scale man is changing his social organization and habits of settlement with great rapidity. The rise of more than 50 new nations since the end of World War II and the new armaments have revolutionized international political structure. A revolution of perhaps equal significance has been the rapid urbanization of all industrial nations. Even the underdeveloped countries have felt the stirring of urbanization in varying degrees. Much of the world is emerging from the simple space relations of somewhat isolated agricultural societies to the extremely complex relations of industrialized, urbanized national states. Rapidity of change in technology is being paralleled by rapidity of social change. There are contradictions within this change. At the very time when international interdependence has increased, barriers to movement have also been increased by the multiplication of national states and the emergence of great political coalitions.

These facts imply that there will be increasingly acute problems as to: (a) how hundreds of millions of people can be supported, (b) how rapid technologic change may proceed with minimal resulting dysfunctions in the man-environment system, (c) how social and political organization of earth space can be undertaken with minimal resulting dysfunctions and without break-downs in the world-wide system.

The very complex political and economic problems already brought forth by simultaneous technical, social, and demographic revolutions and by closed political space cannot be solved in ignorance or by *laissez-faire*. The art of managing man's occupance of space on the earth's surface is becoming vital to public agencies, nations, and private enterprises in a world where territorial expansion is no longer an answer to space problems. Economic prizes in the past have gone to corporations having the foresight to develop efficient long-range geographic arrangements of their resources and product distribution. The social prizes of the future may well go to those nations or societies with the foresight for the most efficient development of space-adjusting techniques, and resource-converting techniques. For the most effective pursuit of all, a sound scientific understanding of space relations is needed. There is thus a vital utilitarian reason, as well as an intellectual need, for space relations studies. As problems of space relations become acute, the arts of space management come more and more into play—rational housing and industrial location, rational land use allocation, efficient transportation network design, and rational area organization for administration. These are practical and humanitarian ends toward which geographic knowledge contributes.

A Strategy for Geographic Research

Even the most promising opportunities or most pressing needs mean relatively little if the capacities to take advantage of them are lacking. What parts of the overriding problem can geography attack effectively within the next few years? It would seem wise, indeed essential, to begin at those points where strengths exist already in the field and to work outward from them. If possible, these areas should already be treating identifiable subsystems in the man-environment complex, or show potentiality of developing the treatment of such a subsystem in the near future. In view of the already demonstrated need of communication with other fields, the choice of the subsystems should take account of the growing edges in closely related fields as well as of the other clusters in geography itself. The bridge position of geography should not be forgotten.

1. A National Academy-National Research Council Committee

Short-term palliatives will mean nothing if they are conceived apart from long-term consideration of needed research into the overriding problem, and design of proper strategy to initiate that research. Thus, as a first step, this Committee recommends that the National Academy of Sciences-National Research Council establish a senior committee of

mature scholars charged with continuing study of the overriding problem
—achieving a full understanding of the man-natural environment system
on the earth's surface.[1] This committee should evaluate short-term proposals such as are outlined below for the immediate stimulation of work
in location theory, physical geography, cultural geography, and political
geography, but should have as its more general continuing concern the
development of programs of research that are adequately broad in scope,
yet properly penetrating in execution.

What are some examples of such broad-scale inquiries? One is the
general problem of *landscape prediction*, as an essential ingredient in
furthering man's ability to manage use of space. What, for example, will
the urban pattern of the United States be like as a result of completion
and operation of the Interstate Highway System? What would wide-
spread adoption of flood plain zoning mean for use of flood plains,
relocation of potential flood plain uses, the nature and magnitude of
flood damages? What will be the effects of continued technological
change and new forms of technology upon the spatial organization of
social and economic life? In turn, what impact will new social and economic geographies have upon voting behavior, legislative redistricting
needs, and the like? Is it possible to predict the geographic impact of
world peace, elimination of armaments, and cessation of the arms race?
What would be the geographic effects of disarmament? The principles
of forecasting the effects of landscape change are applicable to a wide
range of problems at varying scales from communities to continents.

Another line of inquiry for the committee could be systematic
consideration of the *geographic requirements of particular social and
economic systems*. What, for example, are the necessary spatial conditions for movement of less-developed countries into twentieth or twenty-
first century technologies? How could their existing space-utilizations be
reorganized in order to make this shift possible? How many existing
cultures (based upon shifting cultivation, hunting, nomadism, or peasant
farming) could survive? What is the model of spatial organization which
is appropriate to and compatible with the attributes of modern technology and urbanization? What is a proper economic regionalization for
a given set of development goals? How does the model differ from the
reality of today or the projection for tomorrow?

The entire complex of problems of the *interrelations among technology, culture, and environment* need careful study. There is a continuing trend in the United States to use less of the growing labor force and
capital plant to produce the necessities of life. The "surplus" labor thus
permitted by technological growth is increasing each year. For what
purposes may this surplus be utilized and what are the implications for
space organization? How does employment of the surplus relate to
changing military and space expenditures and what are the likely impacts

---

[1] The U.S. National Committee for the International Biological Program,
formed by the NAS-NRC in March 1965, considers an important part, but not all,
of the overriding problem.

of changes upon space relations? What are the prospects for continued under-employment and unemployment and their space implications? What are the implications of the geography of poverty? Can expanded programs of resource development play a role in a satisfactory solution? What are the relations of increased productivity and extra leisure time to recreational space needs? What allocations of existing open space need be made now to assure future recreational needs of urban dwellers? These and many other questions need discussion, formulation into workable research programs, and analysis.

Only within a broad-scale, long-term, context can appropriate actions to promote geography's important studies of the man-environment complex be formulated, proposals evaluated, and research programs initiated. A senior committee will play a major role in the balanced growth of geography and other subjects concerned with the man-environment system, helping to fulfill potentialities and take advantage of current strengths.

2. Recommended Immediate Actions

This Committee also sees several steps that can be taken, to alleviate major imbalances and strengthen the current four bridgeheads in the immediate future.

a. *Expanded Support for Location Theory.* Perhaps the most vigorously advancing research at present is that of the location theory cluster, which has managed at least a partial integration of the economic, urban, and transportation aspects of space relations and has furthered the confrontation of the empirical-inductive and the theoretical-deductive approaches within geography. The Committee most emphatically believes that the past encouragement not only should be continued but might profitably be extended. The basic work in theory and research method conducted by this cluster can have value in problem areas other than the one that has been considered by the cluster thus far. Yet continuation of research achievement by members of the cluster rests upon continued technological change. This, in turn, depends upon adequate experimentation with and development of new computing devices and development of geographic data centers. However, this is presently constrained by a severe shortage of effective manpower.

b. *Expansion of Research in Physical Geography.* Another present key problem area centers on physiography but includes an interest in the climatic elements and in the distribution of vegetation. Already geographers have taken steps toward developing generalizations for these three obviously related sets of earth processes and features, and they already have used formal systems methods in some of their research.

The Committee considers that an extension of work in this problem area is essential to the future progress of geography as a whole. The answers to many questions of resource management approached from an economic or management point of view demand information obtainable only from research in physical geography. For example, what are the equilibria of erosion, hydrologic, and vegetative processes taken together, considering the parameters provided for them by different cultures and differing densities of land occupance? What is the exact nature of responses of any part of the climate-vegetation-erosion system to changes in the cultural parameters? Examination of these questions, originally stimulated in the United States, has produced some interesting developments abroad in recent years, particularly in the Soviet Union. Our own modest efforts in this direction could be increased several-fold without reaching marginal utility. The Committee recommends particularly the examination of this subsystem under the conditions where cultural elements are having their greatest impact, as in regions of dense population.

c. *Two Key Problem Areas in the Geography of Culture.* On the other side of the coin, of course, are the culture processes. Here we would first call attention to the cluster which has concerned itself with demographic qualities, cultural values, and comparative cultural attributes. The study of cultural diffusion has always occupied a place in the activity of this cluster. In view of the development of modern techniques of analyzing diffusion of cultural traits and the interaction between different cultures, we consider diffusion studies to be key features to further progress in this area. We further believe that students in this area might profitably consider for future attention the study of zones of interaction between cultures—like Mexico, or Algeria, or Taiwan, or Finland, to cite a few examples.

A second, and perhaps even more significant, study area would concern those culture elements, particularly cultural attitudes, which create changed interactions within the climate-vegetation-erosion system. In practice this will be a problem to be approached also by physical geography.

d. *Four Possible Steps in Political Geography.* The last problem area which we shall suggest as worthy of further development is that described herein as political geography. Of the four major areas suggested, political geography is the least developed, but it offers definite promise of contributing to the understanding of a very vital man-environment subsystem on the earth.

The first step would seem to be bringing into a closer working relation the political area students and the resource management investigators. The second step is closer contact, or common consideration of problems, with political and other social sciences, particularly in behavioral studies. A third step is to apply some of the methods developed by the location theory cluster to the problems of the political subsystem, especially on subnational and urban levels. A final step is to relate the study of resource management organization to resource use values as studied in cultural geography, and equilibria in the natural landscape as studied by physical geography.

We believe that these steps could be taken if an initial focus in political geography were to be found in the study of the internal spatial organization of a giant state as a general problem, in a study of the interfaces between the political systems of the giant states, and in a study of the territorial viability of small states. We further believe that the past history and present capacities of geography offer preparation for such a focus.

Assets of Regional and Historical Geography

Geographers have one other asset that should be capitalized on. Those who have been interested in the study of a specific part of the earth (regional geography) develop competences for interpreting the physical-cultural complexes of the regions that they study. Students of the way a particular part of the earth has evolved (historical geography) have other competences for interpreting the historical development and modification of a region. These two groups have students that are particularly qualified to undertake the field observation and field study of problems recognized in a more systematic way and to conduct field tests of generalizations arrived at through systematic study, as by the location theory cluster. This part of geography, which includes some of its most devoted and knowledgeable students, can, if properly integrated in a strategy for research in the field as a whole, offer tools of real power.

Some doubt has arisen in the minds of geographers concerning the place of regional geography as the power of generalization on a systematic basis became more and more apparent in the field. There should be no doubt as to its future. The regional or historical geography specialist who has mastered the techniques of field observation and historical study thoroughly, including any needed foreign language, can make himself indispensable if he understands the direction in which the generalizing clusters are headed and relates his work closely to their growing edges. Furthermore, a region may be considered a type of system in itself, capable of yielding generalizations significant in the understanding of the world-wide system.

Catalytic Actions for Further Development of the Field

In the above paragraphs we have tried to tell, in a general way, what could be done. It remains to suggest how it could be done. The Committee would like to note that actions have already been taken in support of at least some of the directions indicated in its discussion of strategy. The support of the Office of Naval Research for work in all four of the major problem areas discussed in this report, and for the Foreign Field Research Program, has been beneficial in post-war reorientation of geography, as has the support of the National Science Foundation for seminars and other activities of the location theory cluster. Nor is the alertness of university administrators to be forgotten. Their willingness to accept and support scholars pursuing the nontraditional paths in geography has been a major contribution. If we interpret correctly the consensus of thought in geography, however, these excellent and appreciated measures must be counted only a beginning. For those who are responsible for decisions in the support of science and other scholarship, we should like to commend attention to additional measures that can contribute greatly toward increasing the power of geography as a scientific subject. They include: (1) expanded support for research students; (2) joint planning of research in two or more problem areas; (3) a research institute in political geography and a research institute in physical geography; and (4) the establishment of three or more geographic data centers.

1. Expanded Support for Research Students

Recognizing the complexity of the problems treated in the subject, the inevitability of interdisciplinary study, and the critical manpower shortages existing in some of the clusters, the Committee strongly recommends four complementary types of fellowship support for research students. These include support for (a) dual doctoral degrees, (b) increased pre-doctoral fellowships in both physical and cultural geography, including those recognizing the important association of the two, (c) expanded field research at the pre-doctoral level, and (d) a system of post-doctoral fellowships to permit periodic advanced training at the centers of most active research progress.

The Committee also recommends that the Association of American Geographers consider undertaking a manpower survey of the profession.

a. *Dual Doctoral Degrees.* In recommending support for doctoral degrees that include at least two fields, we do not mean the devotion of a traditional amount of time expended for the doctoral degree divided between two subjects, but, instead, the training of scholars who are qualified as professionals in both subjects. Philip H. Abelson (1964) has noted: ". . . it is apparent that almost all active fields involve multidisciplinary effort. . . . The situation calls for flexibility and for a mastery of the fundamentals of two or more disciplines. . . ." This is abundantly evident for geography.

Attainment of dual degrees will require a program of support of unusual length, something beyond any program of graduate fellowship support with which we are now familiar. Furthermore, we believe that such candidates should have made themselves not only familiar but also adept in the use of systems-analysis techniques. Some thought should be given to increasing stipends in the later years of such an obviously arduous and extended program, recognizing that family needs may develop. Whether it is political geography and political science or social psychology, or physiography and climatology and botany, or economics and geography, we believe that the future depends very much on the development of men who have not only an acquaintance with but a competence in two or more fields.

To start, we should like to see at *least* ten such fellowships per year made available first to third-year graduate students, increasing later to whatever level the supply of superior students might warrant.

b. *Other Pre-Doctoral Fellowships.* Although some fellowships are presently available to doctoral candidates for the Ph.D. degree in geography, the number of these at present is severely limited. Students having programs crossing the boundaries of the natural and social sciences are often left between the chairs of specialization that set classification and review procedures. Rigid adherence to traditional departmental specializations in educational institutions does not provide recognition of vital cross-links. Fellowships are needed that do recognize the importance of interdisciplinary training, even if it is for a single degree.

Although it recognizes that, initially, the number of qualified applicants may be limited, the Committee recommends that at least thirty pre-doctoral fellowships be made available to qualified candidates through the National Science Foundation for graduate study in geography. They should be appropriately divided between the physical and cultural aspects of geography. A collegiate major in geography should not be considered a pre-requisite for such an award.

c. *Field Research Fund.* As noted above, field observation has long been a mainstay of geographic study. In geography and in many other sciences that share devotion to field work, the problem of obtaining modest support for independent field research at the pre-doctoral level is acute. Adequate field study in many areas in and outside the United States requires funds for travel to the site and for the use of vehicles in the field.

To facilitate independent field research by individuals, the Committee proposes the establishment of a Field Research Fund within the National Science Foundation. It suggests an initial annual budget of $60,000. Awards from this fund would be made to institutions to provide support for field work to individual pre-doctoral candidates. Individual candidates might be limited to receiving no more than $3,000 in any one year.

d. *Post-Doctoral Fellowships.* In a rapidly changing subject there is a critical need for periodic advanced training of professionals isolated from centers of most active research progress. In addition there is need for encouraging mature scholars to pursue advanced studies in related fields.

The Committee therefore suggests establishment of post-doctoral training programs supported by fellowships. These would be available in the subject's advanced research centers (for example, at the research institutes of physical and political geography, at the geographic data centers described below, or at major university departments).

Opportunities for post-doctoral training for geographers at present are restricted, in spite of the programs of the National Science Foundation, Social Science Research Council, and other agencies. Accordingly, the Committee recommends that the National Science Foundation consider supporting at least ten post-doctoral fellowships per year in geography as long as a need for advanced training is demonstrated.

e. *Manpower Survey.* The geography profession soon may be confronted with heavy demands for manpower in research, teaching, and application. It is known that there are manpower shortages in some sectors of the profession, but their nature and extent have not been assessed. An assessment of the present manpower base and a projection of future needs would aid in making fellowship decisions and otherwise in planning training programs. We recommend that the Association of American Geographers consider conducting a manpower survey to measure the current scope and tempo of research activities, keeping in view the field's general commitments and opportunities.

2. Joint Planning of Research within Two or More Problem Areas

The dual-degree training is a proposal of long-range rather than immediate effect in the profession. In addition, the Committee suggests that it would be profitable to consider several other measures. It believes that the seminars which have been conducted in the immediate past to acquaint geographers with quantitative techniques have been very valuable. There may be additional demand for such seminars. They could profitably be supplemented by symposia or seminars with the specific mission of discussing a possible research program requiring the contribution of two or more clusters in geography and possibly other subjects as well. For example, we could conceive of a symposium to discuss a program of research on spatial organization in the giant state, or the viability of the small state, that would include not only political geographers and political scientists but also representatives from the location theory cluster, regional specialists, cultural geographers, and others. Such symposia or seminars preferably should be of several weeks duration.

The problem of communication and exchange is certainly not exclusively one of telling geographers about quantitative methods in geography; it is a problem of using all the best traditions and capacities of the profession to develop a concerted approach to strategic common research areas. The location theory cluster has done this within the area of its interest; it remains to develop still other areas with similar vigor.

The profession, through the Association of American Geographers or otherwise, might well consider the periodic publication of review articles examining needed field research or field testing of generalizations that have been proposed theoretically and have incomplete confirmation from field evidence. Such reviews might be a helpful guide in the award of field fellowships. The important point is to relate as closely as possible the substantial reservoir of field talent and experience in the profession to the broadening knowledge of the system with which it deals, but systems more formally considered than in the past. Stated another way, it would seek to improve and extend the dialogue between the theoretical and the empirical work.

3. A Research Institute in Political Geography and a Research Institute in Physical Geography

The Committee also suggests a third and more permanent action. It believes that the focus of attention provided by a research institute dedicated to a specific problem area is needed to channel the energies of the profession into some strategic directions for research. The Committee believes that such a concentration of research effort can well be employed at this time in political geography and in physical geography. The Committee envisions university sponsorship of each institute, and location at a university campus. The sponsoring university should be expected to have a strong geography program as well as strong supporting programs in non-geographic fields directly related to the area of the institute's problem area. Each institute might well have a broadly based advisory group, including representatives from within and without the field of geography.

It is not the place of this Committee to describe in detail the structure, mission, and funding of these institutes. That can be done only by much more careful investigation and planning than the Committee is funded to undertake. Nevertheless, the general outline of what we see as possible and desirable should be recorded. We shall commence with a possible Institute of Political Geography.

(a) An Institute of Political Geography profitably could commence with the study of tension areas and the spatial organization of political systems. Initially it is suggested that the institute concentrate on the study of three general areas: (i) the interface of national political systems, particularly in eastern Europe, the Southeast Asian area, and Africa; (ii) the internal spatial organization of the giant states; and (iii) the viability of small national states.

The Committee suggests that such an institute be directed by a geographer, but that its staff be interdisciplinary, to be chosen from geographers and other physical and social scientists.

We further suggest that such an institute be located near or at a university where a department of geography has strong or growing interest in the theoretical side of geography, or in systems applications, and where there is also a recognized department of political science and other strong departments in the social sciences. Such an institute can be organized about a core group of modest size, and serve as a "bellwether" for studies on its chosen subjects elsewhere. We believe that it should have a life of at least 10 years, to demonstrate its scholarly effectiveness, and that its annual budget should be on the order of $500,000 (1965 value).

Before the ten years have been completed, we believe that such a group will have had telling impact on our knowledge of political systems. Light will have been shed on the relation of spatial problems to the behavior of some important United States state and federal agencies and upon the foreign policy of this country. Indeed, as we go on year after year, with the mistakes of Berlin and Korea still brought to our attention almost weekly twenty years after they were made, we do not see how the nation can afford to ignore this opportunity for obtaining, at a modest cost, knowledge that it sorely lacks.

(b) The Institute for Physical Geography might have a staff of about 15 professional people and a budget of about $400,000. It should be located near a university having a strong program in physiography, climatology, hydrology, and ecological biology. The Committee realizes that there is a great number of enticing physical geography problems in these areas which derive from the less inhabited areas of the world, like the rainy tropics, the arctic environments, and the deserts. However, we suggest that the focus of this institute's study at the outset be on the natural system in regions where cultural processes have had a long history and increasing intensity of impact. The purpose of this institute would be to develop our knowledge of the behavior and spatial characteristics of the natural system in the presence of heavy cultural impact.

Problems such as land and water use in relation to leisure and recreation; occupance of and adjustment to hazardous natural environments; chemical, physical, and biological changes in water and air associated with urban expansion; consequences of continuous agriculture on soil structure and fertility; and techniques of environmental manipulation to control the spread of diseases, are examples of the kinds of inquiries which might be carried on through collaborative research efforts of physical geographers, cultural geographers, and scientists in related fields. If the Institute of Physical Geography is directed toward such research, the participation of cultural geographers will be essential to its program. Such participation would fit existing interests and competences within the cultural geography cluster. Cultural geographers and other social scientists therefore should be on the staff of such an institute, as well as staff members concerned with physical processes.

We stress again our belief that the results of such research constitute very basic information for a gradual increase of our grasp of the general characteristics of the man-environment system as a whole.

4. Establishment of Geographic Data Centers

The Committee again notes the seminal position of the location theory cluster and the methods which it has pioneered in geography. There are several steps which would facilitate further development of the cluster. Establishment of three or four geographic data centers should be contemplated, located at university centers of location theory where there are available large modern computing facilities suitable for adding special geographic input, output, and data storage features. These data centers would serve as technical training centers for geographers and as places where advanced students could serve as research apprentices. They would also provide adequate settings for proper technical experimentation and development. Even more importantly, they would provide centers within which the data analysis and theoretical dialogues of members of the cluster could most effectively be fostered. Each center should have a guaranteed initial life of at least ten years, to enable research and development to progress effectively, and would require an annual budget of $150,000, plus equipment and computer-time costs.

But even as we recommend such data centers we also note that the methods of quantitative research are subject to rapidly changing influences outside the field which are giving them yearly greater power to deal with complex systems than they had before. It is of the utmost importance that members of the location theory cluster be kept abreast of technology in data systems and analysis. Support should be contemplated for some *continuous* effort toward analyzing the needs of geography in important data system changes, probably through the medium of one data center charged specifically with duties of development.

Geographers are concerned with an extremely complex overriding problem. They accordingly have a vital interest in any improvement in their power to analyze complex systems.

5. A Place for the Unusual Idea

Finally, we hope the strategy we have suggested will not be so rigidly considered by either the profession or their patrons of research that there is not room for the unusual idea. For example, little is known as yet about what we earlier called the "sense of place" in man. Its secrets are still locked from us in our inadequate knowledge of nervous systems. Someday, when the study of nervous systems has advanced sufficiently, a startling and perhaps revolutionary new input may reach geographical study in a full descriptive analysis of the sense of place. We hope that if a geographer has an interesting opportunity with the proper collaboration to delve into the mysteries of the sense of place, he may somewhere find a sympathetic ear among those who have funding responsibilities.

But we also stress that "far-out" proposals may be sympathetically considered in proportion as the field is showing that it has well-defined growing edges. Our suggestions have been directed toward the development of those growing edges.

References

I. Geography's Overriding Problem and Organizing Concepts

Christian, J., 1963
> Endocrine adaptive mechanisms and the physiological regulation of population growth, *Physiol. Mammalogy*, Academic Press, New York.

Dobzhansky, T., 1951
> *Genetics and the Origin of Species*, Columbia University Press, New York.

Gross, A. O., 1940
> The migration of Kent Island herring gulls, *Bird Banding*, 11, 129-155, and many other references.

Hubbert, M. King, 1962
> Energy resources—A report to the Committee on Natural Resources, *Nat. Acad. Sci.—Nat. Res. Council Publ.* 100-D, Washington, D. C.

Kessler, A., 1963
> Population control among vertebrates, *Rockefeller Inst. Rev.*

Lindauer, M., 1961
> *Communication Among Social Bees*, Harvard University Press, Cambridge, Mass.

Mayr, E., 1942
> *Systematics and the Origin of Species*, Columbia University Press, New York.

————, 1948
> The bearing of the new systematics of genetical problems. The nature of species, *Advan. Genet.*, 2, 207-237.

von Frisch, K., 1954
> *The Dancing Bees*, Methuen, London.

II. Four Problem Areas and Clusters of Research Interest

Conant, James B., 1964
> *Two Modes of Thought—My Encounters with Science and Education*, Trident Press, New York.

1. Studies in Physical Geography

Ackerman, Edward A., 1958
> Geography as a fundamental research discipline, *Dept. Geography, Univ. Chicago Res. Paper 53*.

Braidwood, R. J., and B. Howe, 1960
> *Prehistoric Investigations in Iraqi Kurdistan*, University of Chicago Press.

Bryson, R. A., and J. A. Dutton, 1961
> Some aspects of the variance spectra of tree rings and varves, *Ann. N. Y. Acad. Sci.*, 95, 580-604.

Bryson, R. A., and Paul Julian
Proceedings of conference on the climate of the 11th and 16th centuries, Aspen, Colorado, June 1962, Natl. Center Atmospheric Res. Tech. Bull. 63-1, Boulder, Colo.

Chorley, R. J., 1962
Geomorphology and general systems theory, U. S. Geol. Surv. Profess. Paper 500-B, 1-9.

Churchill, M. A., 1957
Effects of storage impoundments on water quality, Proc. Am. Soc. Civil Engrs., J. Sanit. Eng. Div., 83, 1171.

Curry, Leslie, 1962
The climatic resources of intensive grassland farming: the Waikato, New Zealand, Geograph. Rev., 52, 174-194.

Drury, W. H., Jr., 1956
Bog flats and physiographic process in the Upper Kuskokwim River region, Alaska, Gray Herbarium Contrib. 178.

Dunbar, G. S., and F. B. Kniffen, 1957
Geographical history of the Carolina Banks, Louisiana State Univ. Coastal Studies Inst. Tech. Rept. 8-A.

Eagleson, P. S., B. Glenne, and J. A. Dracup, 1963
Equilibrium characteristics of sand beaches, Am. Soc. Civil Engrs., J. Hydraulics Div., 89, 35-58.

Flohn, H., 1957
Zur frage der einteilung der klimazonen, Erdkunde, 11, 161-175.

Hack, J. T., and J. C. Goodlett, 1960
Geomorphology and forest ecology of mountain region in the central Appalachians, U. S. Geol. Surv. Profess. Paper 347.

Haggett, P., 1961
Land use and sediment yield in an old plantation tract of the Serra do Mar, Brazil, Geograph. J., 127, 50-57.

Hare, F. Kenneth, 1962
Recent developments in dynamic and synoptic climatology, Paper read before American Meteorological Conference on Climatology, Asheville, N. C., October 1962.

Heusser, C. J., and M. G. Marcus, 1964
Surface movement, hydrological change and equilibrium flow on Lemon Creek Glacier, Alaska, J. Glaciology, 5, 61-75.

Inman, D. L., 1963
Ocean waves and associated currents, (3) 49-81, in F. P. Shepard, Submarine Geology, Harper and Row, New York.

Jäckli, H., 1957
Gegenwartsgeologie des bundnerischen rheingebietes—ein beitrag zur exogene dynamik alpiner gebirgslandschaften, Beitr. Geol. Schweiz, Geotch. Ser., Lieferung 36, 126.

Kalesnik, S. V., 1964
General geographic regularities of the earth, Ann. Assoc. Am. Geographers, 54, 160-164.

Kates, R. W., 1962
Hazard and choice perception in flood plain management, Dept. Geography, Univ. Chicago Res. Paper 78.

Lambert, J. M., J. N. Jennings, C. T. Smith, C. Green, and J. N. Hutchinson, 1960
The making of the broads, a reconsideration of their origin in the light of new evidence, Roy. Geograph. Soc. Res. Ser., 3, 153.

Langbein, W. B., and S. A. Schumm, 1958
Yield of sediment in relation to mean annual precipitation, Trans. Am. Geophys. Union, 39, 1076-1084.

Langbein, W. B., 1964
    Geometry of river channels, Proc. Am. Soc. Civil Engrs., J. Hydraulics Div., 90, 301-312.
Leopold, L. B., and T. Maddock, Jr., 1953
    The hydraulic geometry of stream channels and some physiographic implications, U. S. Geol. Surv. Profess. Paper 252.
Leopold, L. B., M. G. Wolman, and J. P Miller, 1964
    Fluvial Processes in Geomorphology, W. H. Freeman and Co., San Francisco.
Lettau, H. H., 1952
    Synthetische klimatologie, Berichte des Deutschen Wetterdienstes 38, 127-136.
Mackay, J. R., 1963
    The Mackenzie delta area, Northwest Territories, Geograph. Branch Mem. 8, Dept. Mines and Tech. Surv., Ottawa, Canada.
Matalas, N. C., 1963
    Statistical problems associated with correlation of tree ring width and climatic variations, U. S. Geol. Surv. Profess. Paper.
McIntire, W. G., 1958
    Correlation of prehistoric settlements and delta development, Louisiana State Univ. Coastal Studies Inst. Tech. Rept. 5.
Meier, M. F., 1960
    Mode of flow of Saskatchewan Glacier, Alberta, Canada, U. S. Geol. Surv. Profess. Paper 351.
Miller, J. P., and F. Wendorf, 1958
    Alluvial chronology of the Tesuque Valley, New Mexico, J. Geol., 66, 177-194.
Morgan, J. P., 1951
    Genesis and paleontology of the Mississippi River mudlumps, Louisiana Dept. Conserv. Geol. Bull. 35.
Nye, J. F., 1959
    The motion of ice sheets and glaciers, J. Glaciology, 3, 493-507.
Rapp, A., 1960
    Recent developments of mountain slopes in Karkevagge and surroundings, northern Scandinavia, Geograph. Ann., 42.
Russell, R. J., 1962
    Origin of beach rock, Louisiana State Univ. Coastal Studies Inst. Tech. Rept. 62-4, Z. Meomorphol. 6, 1-16.
Sauer, J. D., 1961
    Coastal plant geography of Mauritius, Louisiana State Univ. Coastal Studies Inst. Tech. Rept. 15-A.
Savigear, R. A. G., 1952
    Some observations on slope development in South Wales, Inst. British Geographers Trans. Publ. 18, 31-52.
Schumm, S. A., 1956
    The role of creep and rainwash on the retreat of badland slopes, Am. J. Sci., 254, 693-706.
Sigafoos, R. S., 1961
    Vegetation in relation to flood frequency near Washington, D. C., U.S. Geol. Surv. Profess. Paper 400-C, 248-249.
Smith, C. E., Jr., and R. S. MacNeish, 1964
    Antiquity of American polyploid cotton, Sci. 143, 675-676.
Stone, Kirk, 1962
    Swedish fringes of settlement, Ann. Assoc. Am. Geographers, 52, 373-393.
Strahler, A. N., 1950
    Equilibrium theory of erosional slopes approached by frequency distribution analysis, Am. J. Sci., 248, 673-676, 800-814.

Sundborg, A., 1956
    The river Klaralven, a study of fluvial processes, *Geografiska Annaler, 38,* 127-316.
Thornthwaite, C. W., 1961
    The task ahead, *Ann. Assoc. Am. Geographers, 51,* 345-356.
White, G. F., *et al.,* 1958
    Changes in urban occupance of flood plains in the United States, Dept. Geography, Univ. Chicago Res. Paper 57, (see also later papers).
Wolman, M. G., 1964
    Downstream effect of dams on alluvial channels, *U. S. Geol. Surv. Profess. Paper,* in preparation.

2. Studies in Cultural Geography

Ackerman, Edward A., 1958
    Geography as a fundamental research discipline, Dept. Geography, Univ. Chicago Res. Paper 53.
Augelli, John P., 1958
    The Latvians of Varpa: a foreign colony on the Brazilian pioneer fringe, *Geograph. Rev., 48,* (3) 365-387.
Broek, Jan O. M., 1932
    The Santa Clara Valley, California: A Study in Landscape Changes, A. Oosthoeck, Utrecht.
Brookfield, Harold C., 1961
    The highland peoples of New Guinea; a study of distribution and localization, *Geograph. J., 127,* 436-448.
————, 1962
    Local study and comparative method; an example from central New Guinea, *Ann. Assoc. Am. Geographers, 52,* (4) 242-254.
Bylund, Erik, 1960
    Theoretical considerations regarding the distribution of settlement in inner north Sweden, *Geograf. Ann., 13,* (4) 225-231.
Carter, George F., 1964
    Man and the Land, A Cultural Geography, Holt, Rinehart, and Winston, New York.
Collingwood, R. G., 1960
    The Idea of Nature (Galaxy Book 31), Oxford University Press, New York.
Deutschmann, Paul J., 1962
    A Machine Simulation of Attitude Change in a Polarized Community, Programa Interamericano de Información Popular, San José, Costa Rica.
Forde, C. Daryll, 1934
    Habitat, Economy, and Society, Methuen, London.
Hägerstrand, Torsten, 1950
    A model for comparison between migration-fields and birthplace-fields, *Svensk Geografisk Årsbok, 26,* 177-184 (In Swedish with English summary).
Hägerstand, Torsten, 1953
    Innovationsforloppet ur Korologisk Synpunkt, Gleerup, Lund, Sweden.
————, 1965
    On Monte Carlo simulation of diffusion, *Quantitative Geography,* (2 vols.), Dept. Geography Res. Ser., Northwestern University, Evanston, Ill.
Hoagland, Hudson, 1964
    Science and the new humanism, *Sci., 143,* (3602) 111-114.

Isaac, Erich, 1959
The influence of religion on the spread of citrus, Sci., 129 (3343) 179-186.
————, 1961-62
The act and the covenant: the impact of religion on the landscape, Landscape, 11 (2), 12-17.
Kniffen, Fred B., 1936
Louisiana house types, Ann. Assoc. Am. Geographers, 26, 179-193. (Reprinted in Wagner and Mikesell, 1962, 157-169.)
Kroeber, A. L., and Clyde Kluckhohn, 1952
Culture: a critical review of concepts and definitions, Papers of the Peabody Museum of American Archaeology and Ethnology, 47, I, Harvard University, Cambridge. (Reprinted, 1963, Vintage Books, New York.)
McBryde, Felix Webster, 1947
Culture and historical geography of Southwest Guatemala, Smithsonian Inst., Inst. of Social Anthropol. Publ., 4, Washington, D. C.
Mikesell, Marvin W., 1961
Northern Morocco: a cultural geography, Univ. Calif. (Berkeley) Publ. Geograph., 14.
Morrill, Richard L., 1963
The development of spatial distributions of towns in Sweden: an historical-predictive approach, Ann. Assoc. Am. Geographers, 53 (1) 1-14.
Pelzer, Karl J., 1945
Pioneer settlement in the Asiatic Tropics, Am. Geograph. Soc. Spec. Publ. 29, New York.
Pitts, Forrest R., 1962
Chorology revisited—computerwise, Profess. Geographer, 14, 8-12.
Platt, Robert, 1953
The rise of cultural geography in America, Proc. 17th Intl. Geograph. Cong., Wash., D.C., 1962, 485-490, Natl. Acad. Sci.-Natl. Res. Council. (Reprinted, 1962, in Wagner and Mikesell, 35-43.)
Sauer, Carl O., 1931
Cultural geography, Edwin R. A. Seligman and Alvin Johnson (eds.), Encyclopedia of the Social Sciences VI, 621-624, The Macmillan Company, New York. (Reprinted, 1962, in Wagner and Mikesell, 30-34.)
————, 1952
Agricultural origins and dispersals, Am. Geograph. Soc., New York.
Sorre, Max, 1943
Les fondements de la geographie humaine. Tome I: Les fondements biologiques; essais d'une ecologie de l'homme, A. Colin, Paris.
————, 1948
La notion de genre de vie et sa valeur actuelle, Ann. Geograph., 42, 97-108, 193-204. (Translated and reprinted as "The concept of genre de vie," 1962, in Wagner and Mikesell, 399-415.)
Spencer, J. E., and G. A. Hale, 1961
The origin, nature, and distribution of agricultural terracing, Pacific Viewpoint, 2, 1-40.
Stanislawski, Dan, 1947
Tarascan political geography, Am. Anthropologist, 49, 1, 46-55.
Theodorson, George A. (ed.), 1961
Studies in Human Ecology, Row, Peterson, Evanston.
Thomas, William L., Jr., (ed.), 1956
Man's Role in Changing the Face of the Earth, University of Chicago Press.

Trewartha, G. T., 1943
The unincorporated hamlet: one element of the American settlement fabric. *Ann. Assoc. Am. Geographers, 33,* 1, 32-81.
————, 1952
Chinese cities: origins and functions, *Ann. Assoc. Am. Geographers, 42,* 1, 69-93.
Ullman, Edward L., 1960
Trade centers and tributary areas of the Philippines, *Geograph. Rev., 50,* 2, 203-218.
Wagner, Philip L., and Marvin W. Mikesell (eds. and translators), 1962
Readings in Cultural Geography, University of Chicago Press.
Wiens, Harold J., 1954
China's March into the Tropics, Shoestring Press, Hamden, Conn.

3. Studies in Political Geography

Ackerman, E. A., 1953
Japan's Natural Resources, University of Chicago Press.
————, 1956
The United States: economic aspects of domestic governmental affairs, *The Changing World,* W. G. East and A. E. Moddie (eds.), World Book, Yonkers-on-Hudson, N. Y.
Ackerman, E. A., and G. O. G. Löf, 1959
Technology in American Water Development, Johns Hopkins University Press, Baltimore.
Alexander, L. M., 1963
Offshore geography of northwestern Europe, *Assoc. Am. Geographers Monograph Ser. 3,* Rand-McNally, Chicago.
Boggs, S. W., 1930
Delimitation of the territorial sea, *Am. J. Intern. Law, 24,* 541-555.
————, 1950
International Boundaries: A Study of Boundary Functions and Problems, Columbia University Press, New York.
Bowman, I., 1922
The New World, World Book, Yonkers-on-Hudson, New York.
Carr, E. H., 1945
Nationalism and After, The Macmillan Company, New York.
Clawson, M. B., Held, and Stoddard, 1960
Land for the Future, Johns Hopkins University Press, Baltimore.
Cohen, S. B., 1963
Geography and Politics in a World Divided, Random House, New York.
Deutsch, K., 1953
Nationalism and Social Communication, Technology Press of M.I.T., Cambridge, Mass.
Emeny, B., 1934
The Strategy of Raw Materials, Macmillan Company, New York.
Fitzsimmons, T. (ed.), 1957
Country Survey Series, Human Relations Area Files, New Haven.
German, F. C., 1960
A tentative evaluation of world power, *J. Conflict Resolution, 4,* 1, 138-144.
Gilbert, E. W., 1948
The boundaries of local government areas, *Geograph. J., 111,* 4-6, 172-206.
Ginsburg, N., 1957
Natural resources and economic development, *Ann. Assoc. Am. Geographers, 47,* 3, 196-212.

Ginsburg, N., 1961
   Atlas of Economic Development, University of Chicago Press.
Gottman, J., 1951
   Geography and international relations, World Politics, III, 2, 153-173.
   ————, 1952
   Political partitioning of our world, World Politics, IV, 4, 512-519.
Hartshorne, R., 1933
   Geographic and political boundaries in upper Silesia, Ann. Assoc. Am. Geographers, 23, 4, 195-228.
   ————, 1939
   The Nature of Geography, Association American Geographers, Lancaster, Pa.
   ————, 1950
   The functional approach in political geography, Ann. Assoc. Am. Geographers, 40, 2, 95-130.
   ————, 1954
   Political geography, American Geography Inventory and Prospect, Syracuse, 169-225.
   ————, 1959
   The role of the state in economic growth, The State and Economic Growth, H. Aitkin (ed.), Social Science Research Council, New York, 287-324.
   ————, 1960
   Political geography in the modern world, J. Conflict Resolution 4, 1, 52-67.
Haushofer, K., 1934
   Atemweite, lebensraum, und gleichberechtigung auf erde, Z. Geopolitik, 11, 1-14; also 35 other articles and books by the same author between 1914 and 1945. (See Whittlesey, D. C., et al; German Strategy of World Conquest, Farran and Rinehart, New York, 1942, 275-277.)
Herman, T., 1959
   Group values toward the national space: the case of China, Geograph. Rev., 49, 2, 164-182.
Herz, J.
   Political Realism and Political Idealism, University of Chicago Press.
Hirshmann, A., 1963
   Journeys Toward Progress-Studies of Policy-Making in Latin America, The Twentieth Century Fund, New York.
Isard, W., and G. Karaska, 1962
   Unclassified Defense Contracts: Fiscal Year 1962, World Friends Research Center, Philadelphia, Pa.
Jackson, W. A. D., 1963
   Part I, Politics and Geographic Relationships: Readings on the Nature of Political Geography, Jackson (ed.), Prentice Hall, Englewood Cliffs, N. J.
Jones, E., 1960
   Problems of partition and segregation in Northern Ireland, J. Conflict Resolution, 4, 1, 96-105.
Jones, S., 1934
   Intra-state boundaries in Oregon, The Commonwealth Review, 16, 3, 105-126.
   ————, 1937
   The cordilleran section of the Canada—U.S. borderland, Geograph, J., 89, 5, 439-451.
   ————, 1954
   A unified field theory of political geography, Ann. Assoc. Am. Geographers, 44, 2, 111-123.
   ————, 1961
   Unpublished Notes.

76

Kirk, W., 1951
Historical geography and the concept of the behavioral environment, *Indian Geograph. J.*, XXVI, Silver Jubilee Vol., 152-160.

Kjellen, R., 1915
Die Grossmächte der Gegenwart, Leipzig.

Koch, J., R. North, and D. Zinnes, 1960
Some theoretical notes on geography and international conflicts, *J. Conflict Resolution*, 4, 1, 4-14.

Koelsch, W. A. (ed.), 1962
Lectures on the historical geography of the United States as given in 1933 by Harlan H. Barrows, *Dept. Geography, Univ. Chicago Res. Paper 77.*

Levin, M., and G. Blackwood, 1962
Compleat Politician: Political Strategy in Massachusetts, Bobbs-Merrill Co., Indianapolis, Ind.

Lewis, P., 1958
Geography in the politics of Flint, Ph.D. dissertation, University of Michigan, Ann Arbor, Mich.

Mackay, J. R., 1958
The interactance hypothesis and boundaries in Canada, *Can. Geographer*, 11, 1-8.

Mackinder, H., 1904
The geographical pivot of history, *Geograph. J.*, XXIII, 421-437.
——————, 1942
Democratic Ideals and Reality, Rinehart and Winston, New York.
——————, 1943
The round world and the winning of the peace, *Foreign Affairs*, XXI, 4, 595-605.

Maryland State Planning Department, 1961
Future Administration of State of Maryland Water Resources Activities, (2 vols.) Baltimore.

Minghi, J., 1963a
Television preference and nationality in a boundary region, *Sociological Inquiry*, 33, Spring, 65-79.
——————, 1963b
Boundary studies in political geography, *Ann. Assoc. Am. Geographers*, 53, 3, 407-428.

Nelson, Howard J., 1952
The Vernon area, California: a study of the political factor in urban geography, *Ann. Assoc. Am. Geographers*, 42, 2, 117-191.

Pearcy, G. Etzel, 1959
Geographical aspects of the law of the sea, *Ann. Assoc. Am. Geographers*, 49, 1, 1-23.

Perloff, H., L. Wingo, *et al.*, 1961
Natural Resources and Economic Growth, Conference on Natural Resources and Economic Growth, sponsored jointly by Resources for the Future, Inc., and the Social Science Research Council, through their Committee on Economic Growth.

Prescott, J. R. V., 1959
Nigeria's boundary problems, *Geograph. Rev.*, 49, 4, 485-505.

Ratzel, R., 1897
Politische Geographie, Munich. (Also 1923, R. Oldenbourg, Munich.)

Renner, G. T., 1943
Human Geography in the Air Age, Macmillan Company, New York.

Schelling, T. C., 1960
The Strategy of Conflict, Harvard University Press, Cambridge, Mass.

Schlesinger, J., 1960
The Political Economy of National Security, Frederick A. Praeger, New York.

Semple, E., 1915
The barrier boundary of the Mediterranean basin and its northern breaches as factors in history, Ann. Assoc. Am. Geographers, 5, 1, 27-59.
Siegfried, A., 1950
Switzerland, Duell, Sloane and Pearce, New York.
Singer, J. D., 1960
The geography of conflict: introduction, J. Conflict Resolution IV, 1, 1-3.
Sprout, H. and M., 1956
Man-Milieu Relationship Hypothesis in the Context of International Politics, Center of International Studies, Princeton University, Princeton, N. J.
Spykman, N., 1944
America's Strategy in World Politics, Harcourt, Brace and World, Inc., New York.
Ullman, E. L., 1939
The eastern Rhode Island-Massachusetts boundary zone, Geograph. Rev., 29, 2, 291-302.
————, 1956
The role of transportation and the basics for interaction, Man's Role in Changing the Face of the Earth, Thomas (ed.), University of Chicago Press, 862-880.
Van Valkenberg, S., 1939
Elements of Political Geography, Prentice Hall, Englewood Cliffs, N. J.
Walsh, E. A., 1944
Geopolitics and national morals, Compass of the World, Weigert and Stefansson (eds.), 12-39.
White, G. F., et al., 1958
Changes in urban occupance of flood plains in the United States, Dept. Geography, Univ. Chicago Res. Paper 57, (see also later papers).
————, 1962
Economic and Social Aspects of Lower Mekong Development, Committee for Co-ordination of Investigations of the Lower Mekong Basin, Bangkok, Thailand.
Wright, J. K., 1932
Voting habits of the United States, Geograph. Rev., 22, 4, 666-672.
Whittlesey, D., 1938
The Earth and the State, Henry Holt and Company, New York.
Wolfe, R. I., 1962
Transportation and politics, Ann. Assoc. Am. Geographers, 52, 2, 176-190.

4. Location Theory Studies

Ajo, Reino, 1953
An approach to demographical system analysis, Econ. Geography, 38, 359-371.
Alonso, William, 1963
Location and Land Use, John Wiley and Sons, New York.
Berry, Brian J. L., 1961
An inductive approach to the regionalization of economic development, N. Ginsberg (ed.), Essays on Geography and Economic Development, Dept. Geography, Univ. Chicago Res. Paper 62, 78-107.
————, 1963
Commercial structure and commercial blight, Dept. Geography, Univ. Chicago Res. Paper 85.
————, 1964a
Approaches to regional analysis, a synthesis, Ann. Assoc. Am. Geographers, 54, 2-11.

78

————————, 1964b
Cities as systems within systems of cities, J. R. P. Friedmann and W. Alonso (eds.), *Regional Development and Planning*, The M.I.T. Press, Cambridge, Mass. (Ch. 7).

————————, 1965
Research frontiers in urban geography, P. Hauser and L. Schnore (eds.) *The Study of Urbanization*, John Wiley and Sons, New York, (Ch. 10).

Berry, Brian J. L., and Allan Pred, 1961
Central Place Studies. A Bibliography of Theory and Applications, Regional Science Research Institute, Philadelphia, Pa.

Berry, Brian J. L., James W. Simmons and Robert J. Tennant, 1963
Urban population densities: structure and change, *Geograph. Rev.*, 53, 389-405.

Borchert, John R., 1961
The Twin Cities urbanized area: past, present and future, *Geograph. Rev.*, 51, 47-70.

Bunge, William, 1962
Theoretical Geography, Lund Studies in Geography, Lund, Sweden.

Carrothers, Gerald A. P., 1958
An historical review of the gravity and potential concepts of human interaction, *J. Am. Inst. Plan.*, 22, 94-102.

Chisholm, Michael, 1962
Rural Settlement and Land Use, Hutchinson University Library, London.

Chuang, Y. H., and G. G. Judge, 1964
Sector and spatial analysis of the United States feed economy, *Univ. Ill. Agr. Expt. Sta. Bull.* 699, Urbana, Ill.

Curry, Leslie, 1964
Explorations in Settlement Theory. The random spatial economy, Part I, *Ann. Assoc. Am. Geographers*, 54, 138-146.

Dacey, Michael F., and T. H. Tung, 1963
The identification of point patterns, 1, *J. Reg. Sci.*, 3.

Estall, R. C., and R. O. Buchanan, 1961
Industrial Activity and Economic Geography, Hutchinson University Library, London.

Garrison, William L., 1956
The benefits of rural roads to rural property, part 4 of *Allocation of Road and Street Costs*, Washington State Council for Highway Research, Seattle.

————————, 1960
The spatial structure of the economy (in three parts), *Ann. Assoc. Am. Geographers*, 49, 232-239, 471-482, 1950; 357-373, 1960, 50.

————————, 1962
Toward a simulation model of urban growth and development, *Proceedings of the IGU Symposium in Urban Geography, Lund, 1960*, Gleerup, Lund.

Garrison, William L. (ed.), 1965
Quantitative Geography, (2 vols.), Dept. Geography Res. Series, Northwestern University, Evanston, Ill.

Garrison, William L., and Duane F. Marble, 1957
The spatial structure of agricultural activities, *Ann. Assoc. Am. Geographers*, 47, 137-144.

————————, 1958
Analysis of highway networks: A linear programming formulation, *Proc., Highway Res. Bd.*, 37, 1-17.

————————, 1962
The Structure of Transport Networks, The Transportation Center, Northwestern Univ., Evanston, Ill.

Garrison, William L., and Marion E. Marts, 1958
    The Influence of Highway Improvements on Urban Land, A Graphic Summary, Highway Econ. Studies, Univ. of Wash., Seattle.
Geographic Coding Subcommittee, Assoc. Am. Geographers, 1964
    Geographic ordering of information: new opportunities, Profess. Geographer, 16, 39-44.
Hägerstrand, Torsten, 1963
    Innovationsforloppet ur Korologisk Synpunkt, Royal University of Lund, Lund, Sweden.
Haig, R. M., 1927
    Major Economic Factors in Metropolitan Growth and Arrangement, Regional Plan of New York and its Environs, New York.
Heady, Earl O., and A. C. Egbert, 1964
    Regional programming of efficient agricultural production patterns, Econometrica, 32, 374-386.
Kao, Richard C., 1963
    The use of computers in the processing and analysis of geographic information, Geograph. Rev., 53, 530-547.
Kansky, Karel J., 1963
    The structure of transportation networks: relations between network geometry and regional characteristics, Dept. Geography, Univ. Chicago Res. Paper 84.
King, Leslie J., 1962
    A quantitative expression of the pattern of urban settlements in selected areas of the United States, Tijdschrift voor Econ. en Soc. Geog., 53, 1-7.
Knos, Duane S., 1962
    Distribution of Land Values in Topeka, Kansas, Center for Research in Business, University of Kansas, Lawrence, Kans.
Kulldorff, G., 1956
    Migration Probabilities, Lund Studies in Geography, Lund, Sweden.
Lowry, Ira, 1964
    A Model of Metropolis, The Rand Corporation, Santa Monica, Calif.
McCarthy, Harold H., and others, 1956
    Measurement of Association in Industrial Geography, Department of Geography, State University of Iowa, Iowa City, Iowa.
Morrill, R. L., 1963
    The development of spatial distributions of towns in Sweden: an historical-predictive approach, Ann. Assoc. Am. Geographers, 53, 1-14.
Morrill, R. L., and W. L. Garrison, 1960
    Projections of interregional trade in wheat and flour, Econ. Geograph, 36, 116-126.
Nystuen, John D., and Michael F. Dacey, 1961
    A graph theory interpretation of nodal regions, Papers and Proc. Reg. Sci. Assn. 7, 29-42.
Palomaki, Mauri, 1963
    The Functional Centers and Areas of South Bothnia, Finland, Fennia, 88.
Ray, M. D., and Brian J. L. Berry, 1965
    Multivariate socio-economic regionalization, T. Rymes and S. Ostry (eds.), Reg. Statist. Studies, University of Toronto Press.
Stewart, John Q., and William Warntz, 1958
    Physics of population distribution, J. Reg. Sci., 1, 99-123.
Taaffe, Edward J., Barry J. Garner, and Maurice Yeates, 1963
    The Peripheral Journey to Work, Northwestern University Press.
Thomas, Edwin N., 1960
    Some comments on the functional bases for small Iowa towns, Iowa Bus. Dig., 10-16.

Warntz, William, 1959
  Toward a Geography of Price, University of Pennsylvania Press, Philadelphia, Pa.
Wolpert, Julian, 1964
  The decision process in a spatial context, Ann. Assoc. Am. Geographers, 54.
Wrobel, Andrei, 1960
  Wojewodztwo Warszawskie. Studium Ekonomicznej Struktury Regionalej, Inst.
  of Geography, Polish Academy of Sciences.

III. Conclusions and Recommendations

Abelson, P. H., 1964
  "Trends in Scientific Research," Science 143, 1964, 223.
Hubbert, M. King, 1964
  Earth Scientists look at environmental limits in human ecology, Nat. Acad. Sci.
  —Nat. Res. Council News Rpt., XIV, 58-60.
Kennedy, John F., 1962
  Telegraphed greeting to the American Geographical Society, December 7, 1962,
  Geograph. Rev., 277.
National Academy of Sciences Committee on Science and Public Policy, 1953
  The Growth of World Population—Analysis of the Problems and Recommenda-
  tions for Research and Training.